PRAISE FOR *THE L*

"No book has made me want t̶ ̶ ̶ ̶ ̶ ̶ ̶
fly quite like Laurence Rose's modern classic as it
chronicles nature's progress from winter slumber
to verdant awakening in language so beautiful it
sings." – **Stuart Winter, *Sunday Express***

"As a detailed primer to the world above our
heads, *The Long Spring* makes for an inspiring,
eye-opening read. And Rose is as affable and
informed a guide as you could hope for."
– **Oliver Balch, *The Spectator***

"Rose is excellent on the science that informs
our understanding ... His ear for the sounds of
birds is exceptional, while his ability to render their
spring songs in precise language is among the
foremost pleasures of the book. Impressive."
– **Mark Cocker, *New Statesman***

"All the 'I's for this one – Informative, Interesting
and Insightful! – and I thoroughly enjoyed spending
time immersed in this book" – **Karen Mace, *NB
Magazine***

"I will dip into *The Long Spring* for years to come, to
sit with the author in some out of the way edgeland
in Europe, marvelling at the many delights that fill
the air, and learning more about this quirky, richly
rewarding continent." – **Mary Colwell**

"Intelligent and thoughtful, and a very good
read." – **Mark Avery**

FRAMING NATURE

Published in 2020 by

Gritstone Publishing Co-operative
Birchcliffe Centre
Hebden Bridge
HX7 8DG

www.gritstonecoop.co.uk

British Library Cataloguing-in-Publication data
A catalogue record for this book is available from the British Library

Paperback 978-1-913625-00-9

Typeset by Carnegie Book Production, Lancaster

Printed and bound in the UK by TJ International

MIX
Paper from
responsible sources
FSC® C013056

FRAMING NATURE

conservation and culture

LAURENCE ROSE

GRITSTONE
PUBLISHING

Contents

THEMES

Loss and recovery

I have never seen a free-born Scottish wildcat and I am never likely to. Negligently and knowingly, we have allowed the Highland Tiger to wane to the point of being 'functionally extinct', as ecologists say, meaning that its small population is unsustainable. Highland Tiger is a new name, coined by conservationists desperate to muster public support for an animal that has been pushed far closer to the brink of extinction than the real tiger ever was. The real tiger came close enough, but when its main populations – in the Indian Subcontinent, Sumatra and Siberia – reached critically low points in the 1970s, governments intervened with hunting and trade bans and dedicated tiger reserves. It hasn't worked perfectly, but it has worked. At that same time, in the UK the last refuges of the wildcat were being desecrated with government support. Long absent from the great expanse

1

of moorland above the treeline, they were confined to the narrow, steep, forested glen sides. By then the government policy[1] of eradicating the wildcat had long been revoked; but the subsidised planting of dense monocultures of Sitka spruce proved more effective anyway. We watched an avoidable environmental disaster unfold and continue for decades in full knowledge of its impact. The wildcat was squeezed into ever-smaller fragments of mixed forest, or pushed closer to the farmland fringe, where successive generations acquired a proportion of farm cat genes, rendering them both impure and less fit for forest life. Today the wildcat, which is not in fact Scottish, but once roamed across Great Britain, is represented by a few hundred wild hybrids and a captive population of animals with a variable genetic heritage.

I write about the wildlife I know, or have at least had the chance to observe at close quarters. Others will write the story of the wildcat, and it will challenge our credentials as a nation of animal lovers and as world leaders in conserving our natural environment. It may have been government and forestry industry incompetence and apathy that finally consigned the wildcat to history, but it is a species with which we have coexisted uneasily for centuries. We persecuted it as vermin from Tudor times and on into living memory, with a Tudor zeal and a Tudor propensity for extreme prejudice. If today's are more enlightened times, then only apathy or negligence can explain how we have come to fail the wildcat. This book is my attempt to understand how and why such tragedies come about, even to this day, and what we can do about it.

More than four thousand years ago, in Neolithic Orkney there was a community of people about whom we know – unsurprisingly – almost nothing. We can reasonably surmise two things, though: that when they died, their families did not bury them straightaway, but left them in some exposed place where certain birds would be allowed to feed on their flesh; and that of the birds enlisted to the task, the white-tailed eagle was the most important. It was the bird whose wings were broadest in span and whose soaring swept it to the greatest heights. Perhaps they believed that the eagles could consume a person's soul and carry it into the heavens, communicating effortlessly between the realm of the Earth and the realm of the sky.

The white-tailed eagle appears to have been talismanic, maybe totemic, but that relationship has been decisively lost to history and to daily reality. 'Totem' is a word loaned from native North America, where the Ojibwe people usually write *doodem.* I think of *Baswenaazhi*, the North American bird whose voice resonates across the plains of the mid-West. It has no words, but it does have a human voice, and a human stance and stature. It will dance like a human when the occasion presents itself. It is a real bird, known in English as the sandhill crane; or if translated from the Ojibwe, the echo-maker, which is also the name of an Ojibwe clan. The Baswenaazhi are renowned for their loud, far-carrying voices, used for transmitting instruction and news as befits their designated role as the chief clan of their people. Fundamental to the North American First Peoples' view of themselves in the world is the power of the totem identity to cement a people to place, and thence to the natural resources and relationships that sustain life.[2]

Both examples are remote from contemporary western understanding. They point to the existence of a deeper connection to the rest of nature than anything our teachings, values or lived experience can equip us to understand. Conversely, as we in the developed West see both our feelings of connection to nature and our direct experience of it thinning out, so we are losing our sensitivity to its loss.

In Orkney I saw with my own eyes the evidence of this deep connection between past human inhabitants and white-tailed eagles, and started to write what was to be the first chapter of this book as soon as I returned. That relationship seems to have lasted for perhaps 120 human generations and been by no means confined to remote pagan societies. Yet still the species was exterminated by the deliberate efforts of later generations who laboured at the task for as long as 800 years. It was a goal that was eventually codified in the laws of Elizabeth I and finally achieved with the shooting of the last eagle in 1918 amid objections and laments that came too late. Later in the 20th century a second 180-degree turn in society's attitude to eagles, albeit with loud voices of dissent raised by a small but influential minority, provided a platform for their reintroduction.

As predators, the white-tailed eagle and the wildcat have seen their place in cultural life shift decisively. The subject of this book's second essay, the corncrake, is different. Although famously elusive, it was known to all country folk from its characteristic call. It was probably one of those species that was widely liked and welcomed as a sign of summer but was just too ordinary to inspire feelings as strong as love, reverence or awe. Its loss was an unforeseen and unintended consequence of the early agricultural revolution. It owes its place in conservation history to its being the first casualty of mechanisation, the first subject of widespread conservation concern, the first conservation-driven target of amateur data-gathering, and the harbinger of the general devastation of wildlife wrought by further agricultural change half a century later.

What farmland birds and the wildcat have in common is the slow and half-hearted response of the deeply conservative and heavily policy-driven industries of farming and forestry to their impacts on the natural environment. The impoverishment of wildlife was for decades treated as unavoidable collateral damage, part of the price of necessary change. This is still the dominant culture of the UK countryside today, actively promoted by global commercial interests from agri-chemicals to supermarkets, perpetuated by government policies and unopposed by the majority of consumers. The rest of us have failed, so far, to make more than token inroads into the default culture of meekly accepting catastrophic loss.

Conflict and Coexistence

As I began to explore this theme through other species' stories I realised I had to include two animals that, according to the conventional systematics of conservation, would not rank highly in our list of priorities. One of them, the fox, is common, widespread and unthreatened. It is of great interest, though, to a cultural historian exploring the attitudes and values that govern our past and future relationship with the rest of the natural world. For different reasons, the badger is, too, but my search for understanding hit a brick wall when it came to this animal. While the fox is an animal I love and admire, nevertheless I understand that others may hate it for its depredations on their poultry and out of fear (usually unfounded) for their lambs. That it has been killed for sport and regarded for centuries as a fine adversary is a matter of fact, for all that I cannot remotely condone the behaviour. As a character in the story of the entwined lives of the human and non-human inhabitants of Britain, the fox is indispensable.

Both the fox and the badger have adapted to the world we created around them and continue to adapt as we continually reconfigure it. We, on the other hand, struggle to adapt to worlds of our own making. Crowding into vast insanitary cities, people became susceptible to disease at a scale never previously known. We developed medical technologies with great ingenuity, only for some diseases, like influenza, to outpace us in a pathological arms race. Many of the dairy herds that were kept in and around the cities were infected with bovine tuberculosis (bTB) which passed lethally into the human population. We solved that problem by pasteurising milk, but the experience left us with a collective fear of bTB in cattle.

Because it is the cattle that are continually moved about the landscape and the badgers that stay in their ancestral domain, the badgers are described as a reservoir for the disease, immediately and by a simple choice of language defining them as the problem. The consequence of this scapegoating has been for the government to focus almost all financial, scientific and political resources onto dealing with the badger, and relatively little on promoting farm-level and industry-level solutions. The result has been described as the greatest destruction of a protected species on record.[3] This seemed to me to be an act of war on wildlife and on the supporters of wildlife.

This must have been on my mind when one evening I was watching astonishing footage of leopards roaming the streets of Mumbai at night. The Scottish filmmaker Gordon Buchanan had captured the thermal images for a programme on the BBC. I found myself pondering something that Buchanan's films had merely hinted at: that despite the obvious potential for conflict and danger, the presence of leopards on the streets of the world's most densely populated city had not, by and large, led to calls for their eradication.

"On the contrary," suggested my friend Sujan Chatterjee, "it's basically a story of tolerance." The word seemed to ricochet off the walls: such an obvious value to espouse, but not one that features often in the western conservation lexicon. I was thinking of following up the leopard story when Sujan made another suggestion.

"If you decide to go researching leopards in Mumbai, you should also go to Gujarat. There are villages there where Asiatic lions walk in and out, ignoring the people, and people walk around ignoring the lions." Ten months later, I was in Mumbai and with a ticket for an onward flight to Rajkot in Gujarat. My visits were facilitated by activists, but the stories that I heard of the urban leopard and the rural lion were told to me through the voices of the forest-dwelling tribal people who live in daily harmonious contact with potentially dangerous animals. They helped me to realise that I needed to rethink nature, and that miniscule fragment of it that is me.

As Eli Enns, a Nuu-chah-nulth Canadian political scientist has said: "western scientists and indigenous peoples come with very different world views. Western science is more utilitarian and sees the world in pieces, indigenous knowledge is more about understanding the interconnectedness of things." I was writing about contemporary conservation challenges, the unfinished business of nearly four decades of my life and I had begun questioning some basic tenets of our stewardship of the natural world. These include the rigorous application of law, policy, science, economics and land management practice towards equally rigorously-determined conservation priorities.

They are the foundation stones of the western conservation model, the fundamental precepts from which all advocacy stems; the source of an almost unshakeable confidence in the rightness of our arguments, and of our evangelical zeal. As a child of this faith, my questioning stops just short of heresy, but extends to wondering: if the model is correct, why isn't it working? The conclusion must be that these technocratic devices are necessary but insufficient in themselves. There is something missing, or something blocking; either way, it must be something cultural.

I returned from India with a notebook full of stories proving tribal people's deep-rooted affection for all the lifeforms with which they shared their environments. The contrast with the institutionalised intolerance of our native wildlife was laid bare when it was revealed that 30,000 badgers had been killed that year – 2018 – alone, on politically expedient but scientifically spurious grounds. At the same time, plans were laid down for another protected species, the hen harrier, to be removed from its natural habitat in northern England, where their natural diet includes red grouse chicks. Gamekeepers managing the heather moors have killed harriers as a matter of routine for at least 150 years, but for nearly half that time the species has been fully protected by law. Conservation bodies led by the RSPB, alarmed at the near-extinction of the hen harrier from England and its continued intense persecution in Scotland, have fought longer and harder for the survival of this species than almost any other. They have waged a long campaign to persuade grouse moor owners to stay within the law, and with cooperation unforthcoming, turned their attention to calling for stronger enforcement, tougher penalties and vicarious liability on the part of the owners for crimes committed by their staff and contractors. The red grouse industry body, the Moorland Association, has successfully resisted calls for restraint and control and instead has persuaded the government to move the problem away. The so-called Brood Management Scheme, where chicks are removed from moorland nests, reared in captivity and released later as adults, got underway in 2019 despite the RSPB's protests and its questionable legality under international law.

The badger and the hen harrier may not have much in common at first sight. The impact of government-led control is likely to be different in each case: badgers may continue to be relatively common in some areas and stabilise at reduced population levels in others; hen harriers seem unlikely to recover to satisfactory and sustainable levels in any of their preferred haunts. But in some fundamental way they are alike. They are both legally protected species officially blamed for problems not of their making. Whereas predators were once routinely vilified throughout the land by an ignorant and prejudiced populace, there has been a transformation in interest, concern and acceptance among the general public. But reservoirs of prejudice persist, and building public policy around the goals of tolerance and coexistence seems just too difficult.

Small matters

Of all the species on earth, ten are depicted here in some detail and to nine of them, I have devoted a chapter each. The tenth has no essay of its own – all of world literature is devoted to it after all; but the story of our own species winds around and through all the others. Many of the nine have some long-understood or easily-revealed special connection to us, but a more balanced account of the worldwide web of life would see this book devoted mainly to fungi and invertebrates, with perhaps an essay on the nightingale to remind us that the provision of joy is one of nature's daily services.

Our relationship with insects can be distilled into the two sentences of E.O. Wilson's apothegmatic assertion that *if all mankind were to disappear, the world would regenerate back to*

9

the rich state of equilibrium that existed ten thousand years ago. If insects were to vanish, the environment would collapse into chaos. Wilson is a renowned American research entomologist who has built upon his academic credentials by dispensing a steady stream of aphorisms like an ecological Dalai Lama. In late 2019 UK entomologist Dave Goulson published a report[4] with its own variation on the same theme: *For many insects, we simply do not know what they do. We have not even given a name to perhaps four-fifths of the perhaps five million insect species that are thought to exist, let alone studied what ecological roles they might perform.* Goulson went on to quote Aldo Leopold: *The first rule of intelligent tinkering is to keep all the parts.*[5]

When it comes to insects, the anguish that conservationists feel about the eroding diversity of life caused by waves of local or global extinction is matched by a concern for the loss of bio-abundance. Individually, each insect species has its ecological role. In many cases, this will be highly specific – the four closely-related *Andrena* bees in Mallorca that are each solely capable of pollinating one of four closely-related bee orchids, for example. Collectively, insects are the fuel supply for thousands of different species of birds, reptiles, amphibians and mammals, for whom quantity may be more important than specificity. Only in huge numbers can insects pollinate large acreages of crops. Only vast armies of invertebrates can recycle leaf-litter nutrients, aerate soil and process animal dung, or indeed the animals themselves at the end of life.

In the modern West, with the possible exception of the domestic honeybee, no insect has attracted a sufficient degree of respect, fascination or gratitude to have acquired any cultural significance. Their absence, on the other hand, is having profound impacts on millions of lives. In large areas of Sichuan, China, a million people are engaged in pollinating apple trees by hand, insects having disappeared from the surrounding intensively-farmed, pesticide-drenched countryside. The impact on the human community, affecting employment patterns, family life and schooling, has been dramatic.

In early 2017 I postponed my decision to retire from a career in the conservation mainstream to join a team drawn from eight organisations[6] who had come together to create *Back from the Brink*, a collaborative programme dedicated to restoring the health of threatened species of all kinds, from bumblebees to birds. While some of the species are conventionally charismatic, like the pine marten and the black-tailed godwit, the programme pays equal attention to the lichens, fungi, beetles and mosses that rarely make the headlines. I devote three of these essays to small, little-known and usually overlooked beings that feature in the programme, and to which I have somehow developed a close personal attachment.

One is a bird so understated in personality and plumage as to have been unknown as a British species until 1897, despite its distinct British form having evolved here, been widespread and, in places, not uncommon. The willow tit is now our fastest declining resident bird, and could end up having flitted in and out of the ornithological record making no impression on the wider public consciousness. Its decline has, however, given it a unique place. For reasons that are not fully understood, it is now intimately associated with post-industrial areas such as closed-down collieries re-purposed for natural and economic regeneration. Such places are transitional habitats for humans, too, as the strong traditions of the pit village communities adapt and evolve. I discover that the unpretentious willow tit is set to become an unlikely emblem for life in the greener valleys of a new industrial reality.

Gilbert White did not know the willow tit, but it is tempting to think that if they had been found in Selborne, he would eventually have noticed the subtle differences between it and the marsh tit, which seemed common there on my own visits. He was, after all, the first person to describe in detail the differences between those other notoriously inseparable birds, the chiffchaff and the willow warbler. He was also one of the first, and for centuries one of the few, naturalists to study insects with scientific dispassion, while allowing his enthusiasm and sense of wonder to remain undisguised. Writing this at the start of his tercentenary year, I reflect on the unwitting contribution he made to my profession of conservation, the very notion of which would probably have been unintelligible to White. My essay on the field cricket, a now-threatened species that he appears to have studied with childlike glee, is a conscious homage.

I have come late to entomology, inspired by reading Gilbert White afresh and E.O. Wilson belatedly; and also alarmed by headlines that in recent years have included terms like 'apocalypse' to describe the state of the insect world. Alongside the field cricket I write about the narrow-headed ant, a species that is found in few countries, and is at risk of extinction from Britain. In common with almost everyone who isn't a myrmecologist, I had never heard of it until it was adopted as one of the Back from the Brink target species. To include it in a book that opens with an essay on the deep history and fragile future of the place of eagles in our lives is to strike an extreme, perhaps preposterous, contrast. The narrow-headed ant is an insect that conforms to Goulson's observation that *we simply do not know what they do*. Ants in general, though, have acquired some unlikely admirers, and inspired one of the most important recent technological developments.

From their invention in the 1940s computer systems were conceived as centralised data processing units, modelled on the best living example, the human brain. Then in 1992, PhD student Marco Dorigo realised that ant colonies were able to perform certain computational tasks, such as finding the optimum route to a food source, more efficiently than any centralised intelligence system. The similarity to certain human problems, such as vehicle navigation and information network routing, struck Dorigo as significant. Solving the problem did not require lots of information to be processed by one hugely capable brain, but small quantities of information to be held by and shared between huge numbers of brains with a limited number of simple decisions to make. The mathematics behind this is called the Ant Colony Optimization algorithm and its application requires the creation of virtual ant-like entities communicating information via virtual pheromone-like signals. Both the 'ants' and the 'pheromones' are developed and marketed commercially by companies set up to serve this burgeoning field and its hundreds of profitable applications.

Hope

At the age of fourteen I was taken on holiday to Wales to look for red kites, and after a week we finally enjoyed a distant view of a single bird over Tregaron Bog. Now, I sometimes see them over my garden in West Yorkshire. I moved there to take up a post as the RSPB's Regional Director for Northern England and was present in 1999 at the first release of red kites into the freedom of the Yorkshire skies. In truth, all the planning and negotiation had been done before I started in the role, but I felt a vicarious satisfaction at our having restored the bird whose Old English name *gled* had long gone extinct except in the names of nearby places like Gledhill. It was a bird that our ancestors had set about removing from Britain and had come to within a single Welsh pair of succeeding.

By 1999 I already knew that the symbolism of restoring the kite to Britain was at least as important as the fact of it. It was not a universally popular decision, and in recent years red kites have again become the victims of a persistent strain of cultural backwardness that seethes with a hatred towards raptors. When once it was official policy, incentivised by a bounty scheme, to exterminate the red kite, today it is a crime. The majority of kites fly freely across Yorkshire and the rest of Britain, but over shooting estates in North Yorkshire in particular, there remains a criminal few who take it upon themselves to deny the overwhelming rest of us the thrill of watching one of nature's finest sights.

At some point I understood that we are a society divided culturally between a majority who are ready for a new relationship with the rest of nature, a 21st century relationship in which people and wildlife bring each other mutual benefit; and a minority who are prepared to shift wildlife out of the way when they perceive it to clash with their narrow interests. Recognising it as a cultural challenge was one of two turning points in my own understanding of what wildlife conservation was, is and will be.

The other turning point had come early in my career. Suddenly in the mid-1980s the plight of common farmland birds rose to the top of the conservation agenda. There had long been early warnings of an apparent clash of interests between agriculture and conservation. In the UK, there was the plight of the corncrake itself, evident to all rural communities by the inter-war years. Within another three decades, and more widely across the developed world, came a Silent Spring occasioned by the drenching of the farmed landscape with pesticides that soaked into the food-chain as through a sponge, killing insectivorous birds in their millions. Later attention turned to the physicality of farming: starting with the ripping-out of hedgerows, then the ploughing-in of flower-rich grassland, the loss of mixed farming, and ever-increasing animal stocking densities.

For me, seeing the effect of wholesale agricultural change on widespread and common species changed the very nature of conservation: what it was, who it was for, what was its purpose; and changed it in two ways. The birds affected by the intensification of farming were part of our everyday experience, from skylarks to lapwings. These were not the avocets and bitterns known to most people only from books and TV pictures. They were not the eagles and ospreys of legend and of summer holidays. They were the birds (and, as we later came to realise, the wild flowers and many of the butterflies and other insects) that in some way shaped our lives.

I also realised that until that point, conservation was mainly about correcting the failings of the past. We had allowed our heathlands to dwindle in acreage and shatter into no-longer viable fragments, so the best of what remained we designated as protected areas and managed as nature reserves. Similarly reedbeds, wild flower meadows, wet grasslands, peatlands and other habitats that had been dismissed as underexploited wastes. We had allowed species associated with those habitats to decline to extreme rarity and in some cases to disappear completely from Britain. So we corrected that by nurturing those that found their own way back, like the avocet and osprey, reintroducing others like the white-tailed eagle and large blue butterfly, and for those that had hung on, like bitterns, rebuilding lost habitats for remnant populations to expand into. In many cases, these were measures that enlisted the support and cooperation of farmers and crofters, eager to play their part in resetting the account.

But that is just one, more-or-less traditional view of conservation. What I also realised was that as wildlife in the human

15

landscape continues to decline, we are no longer just seeking to patch up the losses of the past. We also have to slow, halt and reverse losses that are taking place now, and that we know will continue into the future, for an unknown period of time. This book asks the question – is that even possible? For it to be so, something profound has to change.

At the start of this introduction I described the wildcat as functionally extinct. It was intended rhetorically, because at the time of drafting, it had not been so declared officially, perhaps because conservation is founded on hope and optimism and there is always the chance that such an assessment may be premature. Sadly, the formal announcement has since been made.[7] In any case, the wildcat is the exception among Britain's predatory mammals. New research confirms that otters – the subject of the eighth essay – have almost completely recolonised Great Britain, polecats have extended their range in southern Britain from Wales, and pine martens have expanded from the Scottish Highlands into the lowlands and on into England.[8]

"Unlike most carnivores across the world, which are declining rapidly, British carnivores declined to their low points decades ago and are now bouncing back," said Katie Sainsbury whose PhD research at the Environment and Sustainability Institute at the University of Exeter forms the basis of the report. "Carnivores have recovered in a way that would have seemed incredibly unlikely in the 1970s, when extinction of some species looked like a real possibility."

The first part of this collection of essay subjects is completed by a *thing with feathers*, in the words of Emily Dickinson's most enduringly popular poem.[9] Moreover, it is a bird that epitomises the remaining lines of that first stanza, *that perches in the soul – and sings the tune without the words – and never stops – at all.* In Britain at least, the rapidly-declining nightingale would seem to be a bird without hope, and as one that has itself inspired hundreds of thousands of lines of poetry, were we to lose it, it would constitute an immeasurable cultural bereavement. Yet hope there is, and it comes not from the long, patient, resolute application of orthodox conservation principles. Indeed, the contemporary story of the nightingale confirms the inadequacy of our established conservation model in saving species that dwell primarily in the human landscapes of farmland and traditional forestry. New conservation thinking coming largely from outside the mainstream organisations (and well outside government) has led to a return of many previously declining species into tracts of land not conventionally designated and managed for nature. So-called wilding or rewilding initiatives are challenging the precepts of formula conservation and offering an exciting – because unpredictable – new relationship with the nation's core natural asset, the land itself.

In a short collection of three further essays, I explore alternative ways of thinking about that relationship, and of our place in nature generally. There is a sentence, on page 250, that reads: "Over nearly a thousand years – since 1066 in fact – land-based prerogatives have relentlessly narrowed in scope until barely any of the private privileges of land ownership are subordinate to any of the shared benefits of good land management." While that is true, the trajectory has not been wholly without check. In 1348–1350 pandemic plague hastened the end of feudalism and introduced new ways of engaging farm labour. Exactly six hundred years later the pandemonium of global conflict led to Acts of Parliament that both enshrined the right of ordinary people to enjoy access to the natural environment, and introduced a basic presumption of protection for wildlife and its most important haunts. In our own time, pandemic has visited us again and brought with it the same strange brew of tragedy and hope. For many in locked-down Britain, the unfamiliar quiet has been filled with previously unnoticed birdsong. Children in Indian cities have learned to their astonishment that the sky is a beautiful blue; those in the north have seen the Himalayas for the first time. The death toll is almost certainly lower than might have been the case, when the beneficial effects of dramatically reduced air pollution are taken into account. Everyone seems to agree that an eventual return to normality must not mean a return to normal. Has there ever been a better time to rethink the many meanings of life?

PART ONE

Portraits from Life

ONE

White-tailed eagle

My body emerged from the tomb feet first, face up, via a stone-lined tunnel, at the end of which the sky burst white into my eyes like hot magnesium. Then slowly, blue sky bled back into the white, and a bonxie drifted left to right across the blue, torqueing in mid-glide to cast a glance at my prone form. Bonxie: a modern word, only two hundred years old, imported from Shetland, from Norwegian *bunksi*, in turn from *bunke*, 'dumpy body'. Or more anciently, great skua, from the Faroese *skúgvur*. In these northern lands, names of birds travel by sea.

You lie on a low trolley to enter or exit the tomb, the tunnel being wide enough if you keep your arms tucked in as you pull on the rope that is fixed to the rough stone vault above you; and high enough if you lie quite flat. Once inside, there is a weird sound, almost a non-sound, a feel, of some low resonance emanating from the sea's roughhousing of the rock of the island.

Once, *Iolaire sùil na grèine*, eagle with the sunlit eye, would have occupied the mound of turf and thrift that still encases the tomb today, standing solid like a capstone of rough-hewn rock. I had no difficulty picturing her, for a year earlier I had travelled north through Europe with the first days of spring, northwards until I entered the realm of *Havsörn*, as she is called in Sweden. In the Swedish subarctic, in the delta of the Ume river I heard

....a call that is like something out of Norse
mythology. A tortured cry, loud and water-borne,
from the white-tailed eagle.

There, cranes called solidly and irregularly, cutting through the constant watery murmur from a distant flock of whooper swans. Curlews' wind-song swirled overhead. I was reminded that

....the Sámi concept of realms – of the living and
the dead, the underworld, the middle Earth and the
spirit world; their denizens and tutelars, the shamans
who journeyed between them, and the birds and
animals that acted as guides – may owe something
to soundscapes like this. If so, the white-tailed eagle
is the bird with the voice to communicate across the
divides, haunting all realms.

From there I crossed into the Arctic in Finland, and made my way into northern Norway, where I saw so many, some commanding the air above the waves, most immobile and unmoveable on low promontories or like slowly eroding boulders at the shore, that I struggled to

....imagine living among white-tailed eagles. I
would have to imagine them populating my earliest
memories, and every daily scene. Would I notice
them? Would I love them? What myths and tales
would I have been told about them, and would

I believe them? Have they perched on the same favourite rocks and skears generation after generation, century after century? Is it remarked when an eagle fails to return to its usual perch? Are they given names? Are they guests in our world, or are we in theirs?[1]

Iolaire sùil na grèine would have stood in similar fashion upon the mound of the tomb at Isbister, century after century. She was *ǫrn* to the Norsemen, and *erir* – or some like-sounding term – to the Picts.[2] And back through ages of unremembered tongues, as far back as the time, 4000 years ago, when the eagles were the totem of the local clan. In whatever language that tribe spoke, whatever they called themselves would surely have translated as the People of the White-tailed Eagle. For a thousand years before that, they had buried their most important dead in this tomb, and at some point their ways changed and they started burying eagles here, too.

Freda Norquay showed me the path I needed to take, through her brother's fields to where, in 1958, her father, Ronnie Simison first had his curiosity piqued by the mysterious mound on a raised beach shelf in the cliffs at the edge of his farm. One Thursday, under a bright midsummer evening sky, he sat by the mound, tugging at the turf that grew around a curious upright stone slab. Under the thin soil, he revealed a void, where he was astonished to find a collection of magnificent objects, untouched since they were deposited there five thousand years before: a mace-head of polished black and white stone, two polished stone axe heads and a button of shining jet. With the light waning, he gathered them for safe keeping. The following Sunday, at the end of a long farming week, he returned with his neighbour and brother-in-law Charlie Scott. They dug deeper into the void, revealing a large chamber. With the aid of Charlie's cigarette lighter Ronnie peered in, and watched as the flicker of his flame danced across dozens of rounded shapes that cast weird shadows before the dim light: thirty human skulls. It would be another eighteen years before the site was excavated, and then only because Simison, having several times tried unsuccessfully to persuade Scotland's Antiquities Department to fund a full examination, undertook the task himself. Eventually his meticulous work was completed by a professional team and the true significance of his unique find began to be understood.

"Past that barn, turn right at the Bronze Age barrow and left at the cliff edge. It's about a mile," said Freda. A young American couple were close behind, so she went to greet them at the small visitor centre she runs in the farmhouse and left me to the grass and the wind, both scented with thrift. The path was easy to follow, bounded by wire sheep fences and waymarked at every turn: 'to the Tomb of the Eagles'. The way was also marked by lines of nodding meadow flowers: ragged robin and cotton-grass in the shallow depressions where the soil stays moist; yellow rattle whose semi-parasitic habit suppresses the grass a little and allows other flowers to thrive, like the going-over northern marsh orchids. In places someone had stuck small white plastic plant labels into the turf, with the flowers' names written in black ink: angelica, birds-foot trefoil, grass of Parnassus. This last is not remotely related to grass; its five-petalled flowers are green-veined white, starry against the sheep-bitten turf. Once the path had turned left to run along the cliff edge, the real grasses were wind-shorn and tight to the earth, cloistering the tiny yellow four-petalled tormentil and the tiny white hand-prints of eyebright.

The coastline is a frill of geos, a word that occurs many times on my Ordnance Survey map of Orkney's Southern Isles; names like Black Geo, Ham Geo, Rami Geo, Shortie Geo documenting past associations we may guess at and likely get wrong. It is an Orkney and Shetland word for an inlet, a finger of sea carved into the coastline by millions of years of erosion along faults and bedding planes. Geo geology: the temptation is to assume the same Greek origin for both words, but it is as Norse as Taing[3] – the tongue of land that pokes out in the opposite direction. They were both formed at the slow pace of life lived by rock. As I watched the return of the shags to their hungry chicks on the ledges, or thought about the gradual appearance of summer flowers from under the turf, it all seemed to happen in a blur of urgency by comparison. Yet at the innermost part of Ham Geo, hanging in the wind at the corner of cliff and sky was a fulmar. It was standing on solid air, its pink-webbed feet and its tail making constant minute adjustments to hold it fast in three dimensions, seeking to defy time. It is one feature of the waters around there that may not have been so familiar to the eagle folk: prior to the mid-18th century, they bred in only one or two colonies in Iceland and in St. Kilda. They then spread around the coast of Iceland and onto the Faeroe Islands and in 1878, formed a second British colony on Foula, Shetland. Since, they have spread around Britain and Ireland and NW Europe and across the Atlantic to Canada. An increase in food discarded by commercial fishing is the likely reason.

A few yards before the tomb I let a mother ringed plover divert me from my path. Her intention was to distract me with a play-act, feigning injury, complete with drooping right wing and hampered gait, to turn my head while her chick sneaked into some thumb-sized hollow in the verge. So I let her know she had succeeded by following her a few yards, and resisted the temptation to seek out the adorable chick; I saw him anyway, a day-old the same in size, colour and substance as a dandelion clock.

Inside the tomb I tried to relate the empty space, which under its modern concrete ceiling was just high enough for me to stand up in, to the artists' impressions and archaeologists' drawings I had studied. The chamber that Simison had first excavated proved to be a small side cell to the much larger space, comprising five stalls separated by vertical flagstones. Diagrams, pictures and inventories show they once housed more than 16,000 bones and thousands of sherds of deliber-ately-smashed pottery. Among the bones are the remains of 340 people; there were deer antlers and the rib of a small whale that had been fashioned into tools; there was a dog's skull and bones from nearly two dozen different species of bird. Dominating the array of animal bones were the remains of about fourteen white-tailed eagles, whose talons seem in particular to have wielded a talismanic force. A total of seventy had been placed carefully alongside the bones of important men: one man was buried with five talons, another with seven; while one, perhaps as an indication of his exalted status, merited fifteen.

The original tomb builders may not have regarded the eagles as particularly significant, but over the following centuries this was to change. In 2006, Finbar McCormick of Queens University Belfast and Alison Sheridan of National Museums of Scotland carried out a radiocarbon analysis of eagle bones recovered from Isbister. This showed that the eagles died between 2450 and 2050 BCE,[4] and were placed in the cairn up to 1,000 years after it was built. Were these later people the descendants of the original tomb-builders, or had a new group arrived, taking over the tomb and bringing new beliefs to the locality? Or did new ideas gradually develop within the same tribe generation after generation? Perhaps the eagles had become more common locally, and were adopted as totems as they grew familiar. It is thought the tribe left their dead to be eaten by eagles and ravens, interring their bones some time later. Perhaps as the human population increased, such funerary practices attracted more eagles to nest in the southern islands of Orkney, and they became essential – and ultimately revered – cohabitants.

/

In Kirkwall, across the road from St. Magnus' Cathedral, is the Orkney Museum. I noticed it each time I visited the Cathedral for rehearsals (I was performing a semi-improvised piece with about a dozen other people, some of the sixty or so of us who were in Orkney for a week of music-making inspired by the history and wildlife of the archipelago). During a break in the schedule I entered the building, where I knew I would find another white-tailed eagle. Upstairs a small room about twenty feet by twelve, room 5, was dedicated to the Picts. Its varnished floorboards crackled like a bonfire as I walked over to a large display case, home to a Pictish symbol stone that was discovered eleven miles away at the Iron Age broch known as the Knowe of Burrian. In 1936 some local children were playing in the broch, and found the passageway blocked by a roughly rectangular flagstone, 43 inches tall and 21 inches wide. They hauled it down with a pickaxe, revealing the carvings on the stone's obverse face. Such monumental stones and their expertly engraved symbols are the Picts' most visible and enduring legacy. The symbols are usually drawn from a catalogue of standard shapes, and the Burrian stone is typical, with its three common symbols of the time: the crescent-and-V-rod, a mirror, and a white-tailed eagle. No-one knows their significance.

Approaching the cabinet, I shifted the angle of my view to reduce the glare reflecting off the glass. The stone is not an exact rectangle, slightly narrower at the base and widening towards the top. It has been broken in two at some time long past, and near the base the mirror symbol – an elliptical shape with handle attached – is bisected by a horizontal split. Above it, the curious crescent and V-rod, like some ornate astronomical instrument. And at the top of the stone, facing right, is an eagle, the heavy beak and unfeathered feet identifying it as a white-tailed.

The moment I saw the stone I understood that the white-tailed eagle must have held a special significance for the

Picts, and this was not a depiction of some randomly-chosen inhabitant of the region. It must have been carved by an apprenticed artisan, skilled in the stylistics of the time. It is at the same time both accurate and stylised, documentary yet cultured. It is chiselled, yet its lines flow as if lightly drawn or painted. I studied those few lines carefully and closely. They sweep and swirl across the rock. One runs left from the tip of the hook of the eagle's beak, delineating the top of its head, the nape of its neck, curving down to form the edge of its wing-coverts, sweeping right and up to the bend of its wing, and left along the front of the wing to where it joins the body. A second line starts from the same place, and runs left as it traces the eagle's lower mandible, under the chin, down the throat and breast, tucking between the feathering of its legs. The carver drew curves that mimic the widening and narrowing of line that a paintbrush would produce. He varied the width and depth of the incisions between the eagle's sunlit upperside and its underside. I tried to imagine the light-and-shade effects this would have created in natural sunlight projected at varying angles.

(I saw the exact same image in another place. I returned from Orkney and immediately started writing this chapter. My desk-based research alerted me to a 9th century Northumbrian gospel book, held in the Parker Library of Corpus Christi College Cambridge. The painted image is precisely the same shape and proportions as the stone-carved one. The swirling form of the outline and inner features of the wing have been copied exactly. It is an image shared across a century in time, 210 nautical miles in distance, and a substantial language barrier. Most remarkably, the Pictish pre-Christian image has been appropriated in its entirety to represent the eagle of St. John.)

*

The history of the white-tailed eagle in the northern and western isles of Europe seems to be one of thousands of years of reverence,[5] followed by a few hundred years of demonisation and persecution, during which the species was eradicated from the whole of Britain. In 2007 Derek Yalden[6] listed as many as he could find of the place names in Britain and Ireland that seemed to be derived from the Old English *earne*, or containing the Middle English *egle*, or in one case the Cornish *er*. Earnley in West Sussex, Eglemont in Bedfordshire and Burniere in Cornwall are among more than sixty place names listed. Some may refer to golden eagles, but as Yalden pointed out, most are in lowland locations and many have elements in their names derived from woods and river valleys, more typical of the haunts of the white-tailed eagle. Yalden tested this theory by comparing archaeological records with the place name evidence. Out of 72 records, 57 sites contained the remains of white-tailed eagles, all but a few of them in southern and eastern Britain or lowland areas in the west; and 15 contained golden eagles, none south and east of the Peak District. Given the totemic role white-tailed eagles appear to have played in prehistoric times, the possibility that their remains may have been imported into the sites where they were later uncovered has to be considered. So Yalden compared archaeological evidence with the post-Ice Age fossil record, revealing a distribution of naturally-occurring white-tailed eagle bones similar to that of eagles associated with human settlements.

In autumn 937, possibly near Bromborough on the Wirral, perhaps in South Yorkshire,[7]

....fife lægun on þam campstede cyningas giunge, swe
ordum aswefede, swilce seofene eac
eorlas Anlafes, unrim heriges....

(Five young kings lay dead upon the battlefield, by
swords sent to their final sleep; and likewise seven of
Olaf's earls, and countless of his host)

A great coalition of Vikings, Norse-Irish, Scots and
Strathclyde Welsh had invaded northern England
threatening the newly created kingdom of all the English.
King Æthelstan met their combined forces at Brunanburh
and won a crushing victory, but not without appalling
bloodshed on both sides. And then

....letan him behindan hræw bryttian / saluwigpadan,
þone sweartan hræfn, / hyrnednebban, and þane
hasewanpadan, / earn æftan hwit, æses brucan, /
grædigne guðhafoc and þæt græge deor, wulf on
wealde.[8]

(They left behind corpses for the horny-beaked, /
Black-coated raven to enjoy, / And for the eagle,
white-tailed and dun-coated, / The greedy war-hawk,
and that grey beast the forest wolf.)

The Wessex-dialect poem that commemorates the battle of
Brunanburh describes the arrival onto a low-lying English
battlefield of white-tailed eagles, accompanied by ravens
and wolves. They are the three Beasts of War conventionally
assembled by the Anglo-Saxon poets of the time to clean up
the shambles of battle. As such, their appearance in the poem
may be figurative, a measure of bloodshed rather than a record
of their presence on the fateful day. But it would suggest that
all three were commensal with human death. I imagine them
assembling at the forested margins of the field of war, the birds
attracted from afar by the clangour of iron blades, the roaring

battle-cries and howling agonies; the wolves led by the reek of flesh and blood on the air.

When, and exactly why, we decided to wage 'lamentable and horrible war'[9] on the eagles themselves, I do not know. It is probable that in parts of lowland England, they had begun to decline in the seventeenth century when the drainage of great wetlands such as the Somerset Levels and the Fens began. For hundreds of years before that, there would have been a conflict of interest with the owners of fish ponds – particularly monasteries and the great estates, who could employ men to rid them of their foe. Elimination of so-called vermin as a matter of government policy started in 1424 in Scotland, when James I passed an Act encouraging the slaying of rooks. The list of 'fowls of plunder' to be harried was widened by his son James II, who added eagles and other raptors in an Act of 1457. In England and Wales, Henry VIII sponsored the first of a series of enactments during the Tudor period in 1532. In an interesting repeat of the Scottish pattern, this was aimed exclusively at the crow family, before being widened by his daughter Elizabeth I. Her Act of 1566 effectively marked the beginning of official antipathy towards almost any animal that conflicted with human interests, listing species such as Iron (white-tailed eagle), Kings Fyssher, Ospreye, Fitchou (polecat) and Wilde Catte.[10] The Tudor Acts came about at a time of severe food shortage, but remained in force until 1863, throughout which time parishes were legally obliged, in theory at least, to pay out bounties for every head presented.

The white-tailed eagle was singled out in an Act of 1625, ordained by Thomas Buchanan, Sherriff of Orkney with the consent of the gentlemen and suiters of the court, 'anent the slaying of the Erne.' The parish *bailzie* or Bailiff was to reward anyone killing a white-tailed eagle with eightpence Scots[11] – the price of a hen – for each croft running sheep in the parish.[12] The considerable sum of twenty shillings Scots – the price of a sheep – was paid 'to ilk persone for ilk earne's nest it shall happen him to herrie.' In 1684 the Rev. James Wallace noted that in Orkney

> Eagles and Gleds[13] are rife & verie harmfull to the young store: yea the[y] have been found to seize upon young Children & carie them a good way of. Wee have a Law, yt iff anie kill one off those earnes or eagles, he is to have a hen out of evrie house of the parish in qch itt is killed.'[14]

As the number of eagles and the damage they were alleged to cause declined, so did the rewards. By 1793 a flat rate of one crown (five shillings) a head was offered, later reduced to three shillings and sixpence before Orkney's bounty scheme ceased altogether in 1835.[15]

The white-tailed eagle's long association with humans, dwelling in lowland and coastal habitats, and having benefitted directly from our ancient funerary rites and later fish farming practices, is ultimately the reason for their extirpation from Britain and Ireland. Of all the so-called vermin against which we have waged war, they were the easiest to destroy. Ospreys were to suffer the same fate, and red kites, that most commensal of raptors, came to within a few Welsh pairs of elimination from these shores. Golden eagles, peregrines and hen harriers would undoubtedly have been eradicated were they not denizens of remoter, wilder places. The last British white-tailed eagle, a male,[16] had been widowed eight years, and had kept a lonely vigil on his favourite Shetland rock when he disappeared, probably shot, in 1918. He was already a kind of ghost of his species: a rare *iolaire bhàn* or white eagle, known to islanders to be at least 30 years old. Two years earlier, a pair of white-tailed eagles had bred at Dunvegan Head on Skye, the final nesting of the native British erne.[17]

*

Place names commemorate regular nesting crags: in Shetland Erne's Brae and Erne's Hamar preserve the Old Norse name ǫrn. But from the first systematic persecution of eagles in the late Middle Ages records give only a patchy account of their past existence and their final demise.[18] A pair is recorded on the Isle of Wight in 1780, and several were known in the Lake District until the 1830s. This great raptor of the lowlands still bred in south Wales in 1822 and in coastal north Wales in 1880.[19] By the beginning of the 20th century the white-tailed eagle was almost extinct in Britain, and restricted to Scotland. A few nests persisted on the Shiant Islands in the Outer Hebrides, at Ardnamurchan Point and on the Isle of Rùm. In Shetland up to five pairs bred in 1899, but by 1910 only one pair nested on Yell, the female dying that year, the one whose white-plumaged mate was to go down in history as the last native white-tailed eagle in Britain.

The final irony and most telling testament to the attitudes of the time is that the last few dozen white-tailed eagles were more likely to have been killed because of their rarity value and desirability to collectors of skins and eggs, than as victims of systematic persecution. By 1910, when the onetime vicar of St. Peter's, Maer in Staffordshire, the Rev. John Archibald Sorby,[20] came north to Yell to rob this last Shetland pair, eagles were legally protected from egg thieves by the Wild Birds Protection Acts – County of Zetland Order.[21] The vicar, one of whose predecessors at St. Peter's had married Charles Darwin and Emma Wedgwood in 1839, was shopped by a local and fined £5 by the Sheriff of Lerwick. When called upon to forfeit the egg, the reverend son of a Derbyshire magistrate switched it for a golden eagle's.

*

There may yet have been some lingering echo from the time when the eagle with the sunlit eye still soared loftily to inspire awe and command the reverence of great men. Perhaps some part of its ancient mystique remained into modern times. On 23 April 1919, the renowned wildlife artist John Guille Millais[22] wrote to the Daily Mail:

> From what I have heard recently the pair of sea eagles frequenting the Hermadale cliffs are still there and should be strictly protected...

For nearly twenty years melancholy voices had been lamenting the imminent demise of Britain's most magnificent bird. In 1892 John Harvie-Brown and Thomas Buckley pleaded in *A vertebrate fauna of Argyll and the Inner Hebrides* for 'the proprietor and shooting tenants of lands formerly and presently occupied by white-tailed eagles to take active measures for their future protection.' The new self-made millionaire owner of the Isle of Rùm, John Bullough, was one landowner who heeded their plea, and offered the species sanctuary. His playboy son, Sir George, first baronet, built Kinloch Castle on the Isle, complete with heated alligator pools and other eccentricities. Whether or not he continued to try to protect the eagles, he couldn't – or didn't – stop one being shot on 17 May 1907, and the eggs being removed from its nest on the A'Bhrideanach peninsula. It would be one of the last nests in the Small Isles, but seventy years later Rùm would be the place from which the eagles' return was launched.

*

A generation after the last native white-tailed eagle flew, two cousins were to dedicate their lives to the return of the species to Scottish shores. George Waterston was born in Edinburgh in 1911, Pat Sandeman two years later in Stirling; their families were united by blood and by their long dedication to business. The firm of George Waterston and Sons, stationers, was established in the 1750s and continued trading until 2004, while Sandeman whisky and wine brands have filled the world's cellars since 1790, remaining a family-run business until 1993.

Waterston developed an early passion for wildlife and at the age of 23 visited, and fell in love with, Fair Isle, the most remote inhabited island in Britain, mid-way between Orkney and Shetland. Within a few years, though, he was on another island, serving as a Lieutenant in the Royal Artillery in the Battle of Crete, where he noticed that, like Fair Isle, the island was an important staging post for birds during their spring migration. He was captured and sent to Oflag VIB Prisoner of War Camp in Dössel, Nordrhein-Westfalen and somehow his observations from Crete found their way to Erwin Stresemann, who, though too old to fight, visited the island shortly after the German army seized it. Stresemann was a renowned zoologist living in Berlin, who had made contact with a number of imprisoned European ornithologists during the war. Hostilities were at their fiercest when Stresemann published *A survey of the birds of Crete and bird migration in the Aegean* in the *Journal für Ornithologie*, acknowledging Waterston's substantial contribution.[23] Waterston used his time in captivity to draw up plans to create a Bird Observatory on Fair Isle, and even founded the Fair Isle Observatory Trust whilst at the Oflag. In 1947, the island came onto the market and Waterston bought it, handing it over to the National Trust for Scotland seven years later, once the observatory had been set up.[24]

Waterston went briefly into the family business, but soon decided that his calling was ornithology and conservation. He started working part-time for both the Scottish Ornithologists' Club (which he helped to found) and the RSPB, whose full-time Director for Scotland he was later to become. Sandeman chose to stay in his family's business but became one of Scotland's most active amateur ornithologists, with a particular passion for raptors.

At some point, they started to dream of the return of the white-tailed eagle. The bird was still haunting the remoter fjords and islands of Norway, despite a bounty system remaining in place, more than a hundred years after incentivised persecution had ended in Britain. By 1959 Norwegian eagle enthusiasts were prepared to ransom captured birds, and one made contact with the cousins. Reidar Brodtkorb had rescued a golden eagle; whatever strings Sandeman and Waterston had to pull, they somehow managed to obtain the bird and release it in the Trossachs. Then Sandeman was alerted to two white-tailed eagle chicks in a nest in Norway that had been earmarked for destruction. He approached Capt. Follett Watson Bell, owner of the Glen Etive estate, whose crags, 11 miles of river and pristine sea loch was the kind of landscape that seemed to have been longing to echo to the eagles' cry again. Bell agreed they should be brought to the Glen, and in due course two nearly-fledged chicks arrived, along with a two or three-year old bird that had already been captive for some time. Captain Bell and his family, with Waterston and Sandeman, took the birds into the glen amid much secrecy, fearing sabotage by local sheep farmers and shooting interests.

It was, by today's standards, an amateurish if noble enterprise, doomed to failure. The oldest bird lived off local hens and was so habituated to human company it would pose by the roadside in Glencoe to be photographed by passing tourists. It was eventually captured by the hens' owner. The two nestlings were kept tethered until they could fly, then released to fend for themselves. One travelled to Loch Fyne, where, after five months of freedom, it was caught in a fox trap. The other was seen for a while soaring over the Etive estate before disappearing. In effect, it was more of a humane rescue than a reintroduction.

The official persecution was continuing in Norway, and by 1968 Waterston had set his sights on another attempt; Fair Isle seemed a prime location. Now owned by the National Trust for Scotland, Waterston having sold it to them for the same price – £3,500 – that he had paid for it, it was far from any place where sheep-farmers and shooters might intervene, covered in rabbits and surrounded by waters rich in fish. In June and July two males and two females, all about seven weeks old, arrived on the island to be met by 28-year old Roy Dennis, the Observatory warden. Roy would later become one of the leading advocates and advisers for raptor reintroduction schemes, perhaps because of, rather than in spite of, the Fair Isle project's ultimate failure. Erne's Brae was the obvious site for the specially-constructed flight cages that would hold the birds until they were ready for release in September. Once free, the birds returned periodically to the cages where reserve supplies of food were left for them, but increasingly they were found to be finding their own. One bird, named Johan, is thought to have wandered out to sea and was last seen in late October. The other three stayed together until the spring, when one female, Ingrid, left the island, possibly lured away by the distant shores of Orkney or Shetland. The remaining two appeared to have developed a skill in catching fulmars, and became self-sufficient. Then the female, Torvaldine, left the island, leaving a lone male, Jesper, to continue harrying the local seabirds. Sadly, his favourite food proved to be his undoing. Nestling fulmars, like most of the petrel family, have an unusual and highly effective self-defence system. Their name derives from the Old Norse *fúll* and *már*, foul gull, from their ability to spray a smelly oil from their mouths if approached. All members of this family of birds spend long periods at sea, and the oil accumulates in their proventriculus, part of the upper digestive tract, as a residue from their prey. Its primary value is as a store of energy and nutrition to keep them going over more barren stretches of sea or during storms.

When used in defence, the high wax content causes the oil to solidify in cool air, and can clog an attacking bird's feathers. On 19 August Jesper was found, well fed but unable to fly. He crash-landed in the sea and was rescued, but probably died soon afterwards. He was last seen on 28 August 1969, nearly a year after his release.

White-tailed eagles had last nested on Fair Isle in 1840, a relatively early date, and in hindsight, it was not as ideal a location as was at first assumed. It is too remote: too small to contain more than a pair, too far from anywhere else to act as a nucleus for expansion or to attract new birds in. Another place had to be found, and many more eagles released, or the reintroduction project abandoned. After Sir George Bullough died in 1939 his widow kept the Isle of Rùm estate going for nearly twenty years, before selling the island to the Nature Conservancy Council,[25] then the UK Government's conservation agency, for designation as a National Nature Reserve. Here was another island now entirely managed for conservation, and this time only a short distance from much more extensive stretches of coastline. The third reintroduction attempt began in 1975, and recognising that restoring a population has to mean more than liberating a small number of birds to face the uncertainties of a life in the wild, NCC and RSPB eventually released 82 birds over the next ten years.

1985 saw the first wild white-tailed eaglets in seventy years fly from a British nest, one built on the Isle of Mull by birds that had first tasted freedom on Rùm. Their presence on the island could hardly be concealed, but the job of keeping watch on their breeding was so secretive that my RSPB colleague Dave Sexton had a cover story – he was studying red-throated divers. A further 58 Norwegian birds were released at Loch Maree, Wester Ross, between 1993 and 1997 and in 2007 a third phase began in Fife, with the final Scottish releases taking place in 2012. The hundredth chick to fledge in the modern era left its nest in the year 2000; another 92 had fledged by 2005.

By 2017 there were a minimum of 113 pairs of white-tailed eagles in Scotland.

/

The late RSPB conservation officer Richard Evans expanded on Yalden's place name survey when he realised it may help settle an important conservation debate. During a sabbatical foray to the National Library of Scotland, he saw that it should be possible to deduce the former British and Irish ranges and population sizes of white-tailed eagles and golden eagles by poring over historical maps and seeking out more of the sometimes obscure Germanic and Celtic toponyms that Yalden had found.

In 2012 he published a paper[26] with fellow eagle enthusiasts Phil Whitfield and Lorcan O'Toole which traced the changing distribution of these raptors over three millennia. By adding a knowledge of the ancient landscapes around the eagle-named locations, they were able to assess the likely ranges of the birds, and to create distribution maps. They showed that around 1500 years ago eagles were widespread, occupying many lowland areas, with possibly up to 1400 pairs of white-tailed eagles and 1500 pairs of golden eagles in Britain and Ireland. It was an important finding, as opponents of proposals to reintroduce white-tailed eagles have argued that many of the sites proposed, especially in England, have never been within the birds' historic range. Or else that reintroducing white-tailed eagles may limit the recovery of the golden eagle. Evans's ingenious marriage of historical and ecological information throws much doubt on these claims.

It helped pave the way for the next bold step in bringing the white-tailed eagle back: England. This wasn't going to be easy. East Anglia was in many ways ideal, with abundant coastal habitat providing a steady supply of live waterfowl and washed-up marine carrion. It was where project promoters Natural England, the government body and main funder, working with the RSPB, looked first. As one of the most intensively farmed regions, it is also the natural power base of the National Farmers' Union (NFU). And with much of Norfolk and Suffolk divided between large landowning families, including the Royal Family, the Country Land and Business Association (CLA) were quick to make their views known as well. None of these institutions is known for its enthusiasm for raptors, so reintroducing the largest of them all was bound to be incendiary.

The arguments put up against the plan included the claim that the white-tailed eagle is not native to East Anglia, which Richard Evans's work helped to dispel. Harder to rebut was the alleged threat to livestock. It was known that white-tailed eagles in Scotland eat some lambs, but the claims made as to the extent of the losses depended heavily on which side of the argument they came from. Some crofters had talked about being forced to give up sheep-farming, the losses were so high. Studies commissioned by Scottish Natural Heritage suggested the numbers taken were small compared with the usual high mortality among lambs in remote, often inhospitable places, and evidence showed that the majority of lambs eaten were dead already. Of course, some lambs *are* killed by white-tailed eagles, and as the eagle population increases, losses will increase. Since 2017 Scottish Natural Heritage has been working with RSPB and crofting and farming organisations to monitor and trial measures for reducing losses. These include removing eagle nesting trees in lambing areas, and sound or light-based scaring techniques. The latest trials, which started in 2018, could involve using laser beams to deter eagles from descending into lambing fields, in an echo of the Strategic Defence Initiative, that hemisphere of laser and particle beams that was proposed in the 1980s to enclose the USA and prevent missiles from penetrating, if helium balloons and distraction feeding are insufficiently effective.

During 2009 and 2010 placards appeared along Suffolk roadsides: No to Sea Eagle Reintroduction Here. Pig and poultry farmers found an ally in the *Daily Telegraph*, who were happy to find quirky interpretations of the research that was aimed at clarifying the risks. Sea Eagles Eat More Lambs Than Fish was a typical example, based on findings that in Scotland white-tailed (or sea) eagles eat not many lambs (most of which they found dead), even fewer fish, and lots of waterbirds and carrion. The RSPB turned its attention to North Norfolk. A landowner there was keen to talk, and plans began to take shape, before he suddenly pulled out. The Royal Family's Sandringham Estate was nearby, as was the Holkham Estate of the Earls of Leicester. They had made their displeasure known.

Natural England were beginning to get a rough ride in the press and feared that the incoming Conservative government would slash their budget under austerity measures taken in response to the global financial crisis. They were becoming uncomfortable about antagonising a community that had helped the Conservatives scrape into power. In any case, budget cuts were already forcing hard choices on Natural England, so abandoning white-tailed eagle reintroduction seemed like one of the easier ones. NE announced the indefinite suspension of the project on 14 June 2010, six weeks after the new government was sworn in, and their budget was slashed anyway.

Meanwhile, Roy Dennis, half a century after his first reintroduction efforts in Fair Isle, had through his own charitable foundation found a more receptive community in the Isle of Wight, where white-tailed eagles last bred on Culver Cliff in 1780. Three pairs were released in a secret location on the island in August 2019 as the first step in a project that will see at least thirty Scottish-bred birds released over five years, with the expectation that they should start breeding in 2024. The Isle of Wight offers a variety of potential nesting sites in woods and on cliffs, from where Dennis hopes the birds will disperse along the south coast. They may even become part of a wider population, joining forces with the growing numbers in the Netherlands and France.

TWO

Corncrake

I left Orkney in a Saab 340B 34-seater whose low flight-path allowed me to see standing stones I hadn't noticed on my maps, and to glimpse the megalithic Ring of Brodgar from afar. We took off to the north east, and as we gained height more of the eastern coastline of Orkney's Mainland revealed itself. Before the plane swung round to head south, I glimpsed the little island of Gairsay and beyond it Eynhallow Sound, and across the sound, the island of Rousay. A few days before I had waded into the Sound close to the Iron Age Broch of Gurness with an assortment of musicians. We had gone there on a listening excursion, to where the sea lapped ashore through a sward of bladder wrack and made a quiet viscous sound, like lava; where from the middle of the Sound there came a deep tidal roar; and each time a kleptoparasitic Arctic skua sculled through flurried Arctic terns, a swell of sharp, stabbing protest calls reached us like a hail of flint arrowheads. A mile and a quarter across the water from where we stood, we could see Westness farm, white against the heathery double hill of Rousay's mossland.

881 years earlier, Sigurd of Westness entertained his friend Paul Haakonsson, the joint Earl of Orkney, at his great hall. Early the next morning, Paul went to the southern end of Rousay with nineteen of his men...

...at veiða otr, er lá ir urðinni undir höfðanum.[1]

(to hunt an otter which was on the rocky shore beneath the headland.)

But the notorious freebooter Sveinn Ásleifarson had, by chance, called in at the headland with thirty men, who were rowing themselves home from Thurso to Gairsay. They fell upon Paul and his bodyguard, killing all but Earl Paul himself, whom they captured and removed to Atholl. He was never to return to Orkney, and in 1137 forsook the Earldom in favour of his co-ruler, Rognvald.[2] The fate of the otter is unrecorded.

The plane turned in over Mainland and brought me back along the coast of South Ronaldsay; but it banked at the point where I might otherwise have seen Isbister as an eagle would have seen it. However, this gave me a better view of Hoy, the island where Hjaðningavíg, the mythical never-ending battle between Heðinn and Hǫgni has been raging, and will continue until Ragnarök – the Twilight of the Gods. In 1873 Hoy was home to Orkney's last white-tailed eagles, until in the spring of 2013 two birds, a young male and a young female, arrived back there. Three or four years old, they were not yet ready to breed, but showed all the signs of having made what, for white-tailed eagles, is usually a lifetime commitment to one another. They returned the next year, and again in 2015, when they became the 100th pair of white-tailed eagles to nest – albeit unsuccessfully – since the reintroduction began. As I looked across to 1,572-foot Ward Hill, I imagined the Neolithic eagles that would have nested there, and the fast glide they would have made down to Isbister to attend each chieftain's funeral.

For another two years these young birds would return, set up territory and build a nest. My visit to Orkney was their third year without producing young but the following year, 2018, they would produce the first Orkney-born young white-tailed eagles to fly free. That June I was in the eagles' heartland of Mull, as the news of the Hoy birds' success was being announced.

Britain is the world's ninth largest island. And it turns out that Iona is Britain's 66th largest: being an island off an island off an island, Iona is reached via the stepping stone of Mull. You cross by one ferry to Craignure from Oban, and get across Mull to another ferry at Fionnphort. Iona is where I was heading, and my route across Mull took me along the northern shore of Loch na Keal, heading east, before looping back to head west along Loch na Keal's southern shore, and turning inland to pass over the Ardmeanach peninsula to the west of Ben More. As I drove along the northern shore I knew that somewhere in the hills behind me, in the forest surrounding Loch Frisa, a pair of white-tailed eagles was nesting. Below Killiechronan Wood a huddle of birdwatchers were facing up the hill, all looking in the same direction. I got out of the car just in time to see a huge eagle flying out from the hillside and across the sea loch, followed by another. They were in view for a few seconds before disappearing behind a crag. By the time I had skirted the bay at the head of the loch, where the River Bà empties at the end of its short, winding three and a half mile journey from Loch Bà, and began to head west along the southern shore, the tide had dropped enough to expose a skear half way out. The two eagles were back, standing on the skear. As I had noticed two years before in Norway, no matter the distance, white-tailed eagles command the view.

On Iona, I overheard a woman telling a man that someone had told her that they had heard a corncrake in the fields by the hostel, the island's most northerly dwelling. So I walked north for a mile, along the one road, a lane that runs between coastal fields and the Abbey on the right and outcrops or *cnuic*[3] of Lewissian gneiss on the left. At the end of the road is the hostel and Caolas Annraidh, the 100-yard wide sound that separates Iona from the islet Eilean Annraidh.

I headed out of Baile Mòr, whose name means Big Village, but which is Iona's only one, and on beyond the Abbey where there are only fields and isolated farmsteads, and a trickle of day-trippers continuing north after their pilgrimage. I paused a few fields on from the Abbey when I noticed a pair of wheatears ferrying beakfuls of insects to a pile of stones at the roadside, disappearing every minute or two into the fortress they had chosen for their nest. Then north between fields of close-grazed sheep pasture and flowery hay meadow, the hard heads of ribwort plantain nodding like bees over the grass, cow parsley like fine white clouds over the bees, and hawkbit like yellow lights studded among the clouds. To the right of the road, half hidden over the dip where the landform drops to the shore, was a farmhouse with a vermillion tin roof. A man was on the roof, hammering to a steady rhythm, a flat, metallic clang from the right and its echo from the left off the *cnoc*. Behind the farmhouse the Sound of Iona was flat but rippled, like frosted glass, and on the far side, somewhere on the slope of the Ross of Mull there was a cuckoo, invisible but sending its call across the water to Iona.

The northernmost croft, beyond the road's end, is Ardionra where a few Zwartbles sheep, dark brown and each with a white blaze the length of its face, lounged on the grass with others that were varying shades of white. I walked over a final rise in the machair, a low hillock of pasture that had been muting the gentle rhythmic phrases of the wash of the sea. I sat on the grass with my back against a sloughed-away cliff of shell sand and listened; and studied the coastline, and the dozens of islets and small islands, the sounds and inlets, and the distant Munros. Grey seals plied right to left – south east to north west – along Caolas Annraidh, a gannet passed that way too. The quadrant of sea that was visible from that spot appeared ringed with islands. In reality they lay offshore at varying distances, and the ring was an illusion seen only at sea level. I drew their distinct, differing silhouettes so that I could check their identity, and found they were, from left to right:

Southern Treshnish Islands of Lunga and Bad Mor and Bad Beag: 8 miles north-northwest

Northern Treshnish Islands including distinctive Fladda ('Flat Island'): 10.6 miles north by west

Staffa: 5.9 miles north-northeast

Little Colonsay: 8.2 miles northeast by north

The soundscape was of meadow pipits and skylarks behind me to landward, ringed plovers and oystercatchers in the foreground, an occasional kittiwake chorus from the rocks of Eilean Annraidh, and the antiphony of one run of the sea on the *eilean*, against another run on the point itself. That is what is called the 'sing of the shore' in some parts, intelligible to seafarers who gauge their position by it in darkness or fog. A whimbrel chased another along the *caolas* with a six-note semi-trill, a common gull yapped like a puppy. In a neighbouring two-foot high sand cliff was a 'colony' of one sand martin nest. Eight rooks from their own colony a mile away at the Parish Church were working the machair like choughs. The nearest real choughs are 18 miles away on Colonsay, but here a song thrush sang with a mimicked chough-call slipped in to the melody: the one must have visited the other at some time. I was unable to detect the sound I was listening hardest for, the metronomic double rasp of the corncrake from the meadows by the hostel.

On the way back, I stopped to watch the wheatears who had not let up in their industry of feeding visits to the pile of stones. As I drew closer I noticed two chicks were out of the nest, camouflaged in dull grey-brown against the stones and at most a day short of fledging. Behind, in the Sound of Iona five bottle-nosed dolphins cruised unhurriedly northwards, breaking the surface every ten seconds or so with their gently undulating rolls.

Imagine living in a place where the cheerful, cheering *tzchaarr* of breeding starlings is still everywhere to be heard, as it should still be over the whole country.[4] They busied about in families and small groups. The young birds were the colour of dark cocoa: all round the half-ring of islands off the west and north coasts the starlings are distinctly different from mainland birds. In Shetland they are larger; in the Outer Hebrides they are intermediate in size. Here in the Inner Hebrides they seem similar in size to mainland birds, but share the dark juvenile coloration of all the island forms. There were many nests about the island still occupied: one in the sign of the Argyll Hotel, below my room window looking out on the harbour; one low down in the wall around the Parish Church grounds, no more than four feet off the ground; one in an unfinished new-build house, one in a redundant concrete gate-post.

If I had not stopped to watch the wheatears I may have missed hearing a corncrake in the adjacent field. About two acres in extent, the nearer (western) half sloped gently toward the shore and comprised improved pasture with two small patches of nettles. The sound came from the far end, beyond where the field drops again, via two shelves of land which hid from view a rushier, wetter, iris-clad eastern half. They are night-callers mostly, and I heard only three short bursts of four paired rasps in the space of about half an hour. I decided to return at dusk to the place I decided was to be called Lost Glove Field, someone having planted a plum-coloured chenille glove over the top of a fence-post, like a permanent raised-hand greeting at the gate.

I spent the afternoon on the western shore, wondering if I might see an otter, or whether the heat might keep them in their lay-ups and holts. The gneiss outcrops are connected by saddle-shaped sweeps of machair[5] grass to landward, small bays of cobble at the shore. I descended into one. The rock echoed the calls and song of a rock pipit; he and a meadow pipit that parachuted over the grass at the back of the bay each sang a variation on the other's theme. The bay's smooth contours were marked by sweeps of concentric strandlines comprising air-crisped wrack and mummified kelp stalks.

Two female ringed plovers guided me up-shore, away from their nests, past a pile of broken and abandoned lobster creels, drawn up above the high water line in a past clean-up, above the zone where silverweed studded the cobbles with yellow, and onto the machair where sheep tended a lawn of red fescue. A pair of fledgling wheatears awaited their next feed at the entrance to a rabbit burrow. One slipped into the burrow as I approached, the other stood watching me. The shyer sibling soon returned when its parent arrived with the latest insect catch. Another two fledglings at the edge of another burrow-nest bobbed and scolded with a muffled version of a stonechat's pebble-strike call.

Between the gneiss *cnuic* the grassland was rippled by its past as 'lazybed' farmland, allocated under the runrig system. Daisies and buttercups picked out the rigs and the furrows. Beneath the surface is pebbly sand, easily exposed by excessive grazing and hoof-wear, or by rabbits scraping for roots or burrow-making. Where slabs of steep ground had sloughed off, the sand-face tenement was shared between rabbits and, in a few places, sand martins.

A pair of twite gleaning seeds in the short-grass meadow. As I watched, the streaky, linnet-like finches of the isles flew up onto the side of a *cnoc*, and a female wheatear flew towards and then around me in a tight circle, scolding harshly. Another youngster was nearby, where three rocks, probably ancient tumbles from an eroding *cnoc*, formed a kind of natural dolmen, with a cleft where the young wheatear was waiting for his mother to stop attending to me, and resume attendance to him.

I wondered whether wheatears somehow and for some reason synchronise their breeding. It's a thought that was corroborated by each new sighting: four siblings at the mouth of a rabbit burrow in the side of a small knoll, and two lots of two a hundred yards apart in a large field opposite Skerryvore; they all seemed to be exactly the same age. I reflected on the sheer density of grassland insectivores. Wheatears, starlings, pied wagtails, meadow pipits, rock pipits, skylarks.

I was on the island for two nights, and for the second night I moved to a B&B on the machair. There was a wheatear nest across the lane from there, and I was watching yet another family in their last day or two of occupation when I heard a corncrake in the distance. I doubled back a hundred yards or so to try to triangulate the sound, which seemed to come from a long-grass meadow at Culbiurg, the westernmost farm.

Back at Lost Glove Field, I was struck by the difference the low setting sun, behind me to the west, made as I looked east to the Ross of Mull. Out of the flat, Hokusai blues of nine hours before, emerged 3D contours in high definition, islets and rocks of pink granite in a landscape palette of ochres and greens.

I heard no corncrake, and walked south towards the island's jetty, only for the double rasp to reach me when I arrived, from the direction from which I had just come. It sounded closer than the Abbey, perhaps even in the gardens that separate the only street in the village from the shore. As ever, though, the closer I got to what I thought was the source, the farther away it seemed. I followed a green lane from the end of the village street northwards and finally pinned it down to the field in front of the Abbey. As I approached, the crex-crex became a counterpoint of two double calls, the second on the offbeat of the first. A second bird was in the neighbouring field, which in turn was bounded on the far side by Lost Glove Field, whose own corncrake's distant cry had also started up.

The near bird seemed to be calling from a patch of nettles and yellow flag irises that was growing around a collection of whitish rounded boulders. A pair of wheatears was flitting amongst the boulders, with two newly fledged young to feed, separated by the Lost Glove Field wheatear nest by 475 yards. The farthest corncrake would call from Lost Glove Field, and the middle bird, about 80 yards away, would respond, prompting the Abbey bird to join in.

I walked back to Skerryvore. At 2245 I passed the island's fire station and its adjoining hayfield where another corncrake was singing. Into a soft pink dusk, a song thrush sang against the sea's slow licking. Turning right along the Machair road, where a snipe tick-tocked, counting down the light and a sixth corncrake called from the south, from somewhere this side of Sròn Iolare – Eagle Promontory.

It is a sound that Robert Henryson will have known. His 1480s fable *The Preaching of the Swallow*, written in Middle Scots, contains one of the earliest literary references to the bird he called the quailzie:

> The year wore on, till came the June month fair,
> And all the seeds the previous year had borne
> Had sprouted high enough to hide a hare
> Or corncrake, craking loudly in the corn.
> I travelled on from afternoon till morn,
> Toward the hedge, under the hawthorn green,
> Where I that wondrous flock of birds had seen.[6]

Linnaeus will have heard it. Κρεξ κρεξ ... κρεξ κρεξ ... κρεξ κρεξ ... κρεξ κρεξ ... κρεξ κρεξ ... κρεξ κρεξ ... κρεξ κρεξ ... from the meadows throughout Småland. After dark, labouring by candlelight over his monumental *Systema Naturae*, he would have heard it on summer nights, calling from the meadows beyond his open window. When he came to choose a name for the bird he described as *Corpus valde compressum; vesperi & nocti sonorus voce ingeminata crex*,[7] the onomatopoeic κρεξ of Ancient Greece would have been suggested by the bird itself. *Rallus crex*, then, the rail that crakes, he baptised it in 1758. But as Linnaeus himself noted, the crake – the call – is always duple, and it was inevitable that taxonomy, eponymy and onomatopoeia would converge upon *Crex crex*, after Johann Matthäus Bechstein deemed, in 1803, that the species was too distantly related to *Rallus*, and merited its own generic name.

To my ear, it is a sound with no vowel: 'crrkk'.

It was a sound that emanated from the hay, from every field, it seemed, from Norway to France and France to Russia. But it was also a kind of living doubt, in John Clare's words, its very existence uncertain. "We know 'tis something," he wrote, "but it ne'er will blab the secret out."[8] In another poem, he noted that upon its arrival in May

That feather'd spirit stops the swain
To listen to his note again
And school boy still in vain retraces
The secrets of his hiding places[9]

For while the corncrake was heard everywhere, it was seen nowhere. Richard Jeffries noted, in 1880, that the corncrake and the grasshopper warbler (which he called the grasshopper lark) "are so characteristic of the meadows in southwestern counties that a summer evening seems silent to me without the 'crake, crake!' of the one and the singular sibilous rattle of the other." He was comparing his former home in Wiltshire with Surbiton, now a suburb of London, where he moved in 1877. Whilst he seldom heard it from the thoroughfare he called Nightingale Road "they come to other places not far distant from the road."[10]

In D.H. Lawrence's *Sons and Lovers*, Gertrude Morel has been locked out of her house by her drunken husband. She is in the scented darkness of her own garden, her young sons in bed inside the house, her husband asleep, head and arms sprawled across the kitchen table. "The night was very large, and very strange, stretching its hoary distances infinitely. And out of the silver-grey fog of darkness came sounds vague and hoarse: a corncrake not far off, sound of a train like a sigh, and distant shouts of men."[11] The bird returns 250 pages later:

A corncrake in the hay-close called insistently. The
moon slid quite quickly downwards, growing more
flushed. Behind him the great flowers leaned as if
they were calling. And then, like a shock, he caught
another perfume, something raw and coarse. Hunting
round, he found the purple iris, touched their fleshy
throats and their dark, grasping hands. At any rate,
he had found something. They stood stiff in the
darkness. Their scent was brutal. The moon was

> melting down upon the crest of the hill. It was gone;
> all was dark. The corncrake called still.

It recurs elsewhere in Lawrence's work. In *The White Peacock*[12] the monotonous voice that had once contained 'pleasant notes of romance' had become intolerable 'like the voice of fate speaking out its tuneless perseverance in the night.' In *The Rainbow*[13] Ursula Brangwen feels the same ambivalence at the sounds of summer, when superimposed on her own self-doubt: 'what good was it that it was summer, that right till evening, when the corncrakes called, the larks would mount up into the light, to sing once more before nightfall.'

> The moon lies back and reddens.
> In the valley a corncrake calls
> Monotonously,
> With a plaintive, unalterable voice, that deadens
> My confident activity;
> With a hoarse, insistent request that falls
> Unweariedly, unweariedly,
> Asking something more of me,
> Yet more of me.[14]

The sense Lawrence creates of the call being an essential and inescapable element of the nocturnal landscape echoes another John Clare poem from 70 years earlier. *The Corn Craik's Rispy Song* is about a girl, yet it is the bird – and in particular its song – that inhabits the poem as thoroughly as it does the landscape, with the two human protagonists merely passing through the scene and the sound. In Clare's Northamptonshire, Jefferies's Wiltshire and Surrey and Lawrence's Nottinghamshire, the corncrake was ubiquitous. And so much so across the whole country, that it would not be difficult to compile a historical atlas of its distribution based on literary references:

In Jerome K. Jerome's *Three Men in a Boat* of 1889, George, Harris and "J" imagine what it will be like to camp on the bank of the Thames on their journey from Kingston to Oxford and back. "Slowly the golden memory of the dead sun fades from the hearts of the cold, sad clouds. Silent, like sorrowing children, the birds have ceased their song, and only the moorhen's plaintive cry and the harsh croak of the corncrake stirs the awed hush around the couch of waters, where the dying day breathes out her last." Jerome's and Lawrence's fictional corncrakes sang from real places and the authors' lived experience, but the bird is also to be heard in landscapes of pure imagination, such as Elizabeth Gaskell's vaguely Midlands setting in *Wives and Daughters* (beautifully presaging its presence in *Sons and Lovers*):

> ...and then the maids and men trooped in to prayers
> – the windows were still open, and the sounds of the
> solitary corncrake, and the owl hooting in the trees,
> mingled with the words spoken. Then to bed; and so
> ended the day.

That it was vulnerable, especially at haymaking time, had been documented since at least 1651, when Andrew Marvell wrote of the mowers in the countryside near York:

> With whistling Sithe, and Elbow strong,
> These Massacre the Grass along:
> While one, unknowing, carves the Rail,
> Whose yet unfeather'd Quils her fail.
> The Edge all bloody from its Breast
> He draws, and does his stroke detest;
> Fearing the Flesh untimely mow'd
> To him a Fate as black forebode.[15]

His compassion for the unfledged landrail, as the corncrake was then called, is borne of a sense that all flesh is as grass

– the bird dies too soon, and the young mower fears an omen for himself. It must have been a regular occupational hazard. Arriving at night from Congo[16] in late April and May, corncrakes would invariably seek out overgrown corners of fields, the nettle-beds and tangles of cow parsley that provided cover in the early spring, before the hay and the wheat had grown. As soon as the fields provided enough of a sward to keep the birds hidden from view, they would spread into the grasslands. The males would each select a small area from which to sing, and do so insistently for about four hours each night, until they had attracted a mate. Thereafter they would sing on through the summer, only slightly less intensely. Their attachment to tall grass was so strong, that at mowing time they would creep away from the feet of the mowers, sticking to any remaining standing vegetation, until they had no choice but to fly, or to dash to the nearest cover at the edges of the fields.

On a good day, one man could scythe and rake an acre of hay,[17] enough to feed a horse for half the winter. But haymaking was usually a communal affair: in about 1715 an unknown painter recorded a scene at Dixton Manor in Gloucestershire. Looking north from the Cotswold escarpment to Bredon Hill, with nearby Alderton Hill on the right and Knolls Camp Hill on the left, this vast canvas shows Mickle Mead, an unenclosed meadow of about 30 acres near the village of Stanley Pontlarge. Still traceable on Google Earth today, the meadow was divided into square plots belonging to a few wealthy families, including the Higfords of Dixton Manor. That haymaking was a vast communal enterprise is clearly evident in the painting, which in fact depicts several simultaneous activities that would in reality have been carried out a few days apart, such as scything, tedding and gathering. In the scene are at least 71 men and 62 women striving to bring in the hay before the scudding clouds arrive.[18]

Then from the 1840s onwards, the first horse-drawn mowers enabled one man to produce seven times as much. Despite the increased speed of the cut, this might have made it easier for the corncrakes to escape harm: the machines followed a predictable line, whereas evading the sweeping scythes of a gang of men in a field would have caused chaos and panic. However, within a few decades of the new innovation people started to notice a drop in corncrake numbers. On Monday, June 29 1903 an agriculture columnist wrote in *The Times:*

In a day or two we pass into the second half of the year, and the cuckoo will be preparing to fly to his southern home. The corncrake or landrail, a very useful bird, seems to become scarcer each season, and its raucous call that used to be a familiar sound on a June evening is heard less and less. It has been suggested that the increasing use of mowing machines and reapers with their incessant rattle and their cruel knives, has frightened the bird away.

Local papers chronicled the decline across the country. In late July 1909 a correspondent to the *Barnsley Chronicle*[19] noted:

During the last few days I have heard the harsh cry of the corncrake. His domestic duties are over for the year. Reaping machines have invaded his domain, and throughout the day he seeks the silence and shelter of the corn. But in the twilights of morning and evening the corncrake fares afield to search for the food on which his heart is set.

Over the next two decades more letters would appear in local papers. One Henry Walker of Dale View, Bradwell was a regular correspondent to the *Sheffield Daily Telegraph.* On 7 July 1928 he wrote:

It is a matter of keen regret to English naturalists that one of our most interesting ornithological specimens in the shape of the corncrake is gradually becoming extinct.... A few years ago five or six could be heard simultaneously almost anywhere in a meadowland neighbourhood.

Mr. Walker attributed their decline to two things: the decline locally in corn production, leaving only hay fields to nest in, and the loss of eggs and young birds to the mowing-machines. In the 1920s, corn was reaped much later than hay, when the young were big enough to make their escape. He made the same point in the same paper on 11 June the following year, prompting someone who signed themselves "E.S." to disagree:

I do not share the pessimistic view held by your correspondent, Henry Walker, that the corncrake is doomed to extinction. For twenty years I have visited places within a radius of six to eight miles of the Town Hall, and have found the corncrake in the same old spots year after year.[20]

It was during these decades that a growing network of amateur ornithologists was coalescing into local societies and publishing county and district avifaunas – books compiling the known information on the status of every bird to have occurred in the area in question. The often very local perspectives of people like Messrs. Walker and "E.S." could be put into a wider context. Some comprised extensive surveys compiled from the collected records of dozens of expert correspondents. Many of the early ones were the work of one or two men whose personal observations and recollections were of variable reliability. There were no coordinated surveys of the kind thousands of amateurs participate in today, and that form the basis of our modern understanding of the distribution, abundance and population trends of the UK's birds. But despite their uneven quality, the avifaunas published between about 1880 and 1920 paint a clear and consistent picture for one species whose presence, absence and approximate abundance is not difficult to assess: the corncrake or landrail.

One of the most comprehensive collections of such books is at the Headquarters of the RSPB, in Sandy, Bedfordshire. I worked there from 1983 to 1999 before moving north to a small regional office in Denby Dale, where I have been based since. My visits to HQ rarely allow much time for browsing old books, but one day I decided to take a day off work, and to spend it in the RSPB Library. It is located in the former billiard room of The Lodge, the neo-Tudor house built in 1870 by Henry Clutton for Arthur Wellesley Peel. The room measures about thirty feet by twenty and its walls are wood panelled with tall, narrow cupboards built into alcoves, where the billiard cues were kept. About 35 feet of shelf space is devoted to the avifaunas, arranged in geographical order, starting with *The Birds of the West of Scotland*, written in 1871 by R. Gray, high and to the left, and finishing with *Birding in Pembrokeshire* of 2004 by Jonathan Green and Owen Roberts, at knee height on the right. Before me at waist height was Thomas Hudson Nelson's two-volume *Birds of Yorkshire*, published in 1907. To its left was John Mather's 1986 book of the same title. The earlier work described the corncrake as "generally distributed, common except in manufacturing districts". Mather's matter-of-fact chronicling of the bird's disappearance from the county over the intervening eight decades is chilling: already becoming scarce in the East Riding by 1907; almost disappeared from the Wolds by 1909; and all but lost from all lowland areas by 1924. In the higher ground of the Dales, where hay-cutting generally took place a few weeks later, allowing more young birds to fledge, it persisted for another decade. By the 1950s, records of breeding birds were so sparse that Mather lists them all.

Next I took down Joseph Whitaker's *Notes on the Birds of Nottinghamshire*, also dating from 1907, and *The Birds of Nottinghamshire*, edited in 1975 by Austen Dobbs for the Trent Valley Birdwatchers. Whitaker was a gentleman naturalist and fieldsportsman, born in 1850 and living most of his life at Blidworth, about 12 miles from D.H. Lawrence's Eastwood. Of the corncrake (after noting that its local name was Meadow Drake), he writes:

> I sorrow to say this interesting bird is a rapidly diminishing species, not only as far as Notts. is concerned, but in many other counties. Twenty years back it was the exception in the spring not to hear a Crake in nearly every mowing-field in the Trent Valley, and almost every seed and grass field left for hay in other parts. In this very high and dry parish we had from ten to fifteen pairs, now for the last three years not a bird has been heard....

> ....I fancy the mowing machine has something to do with it, going round and round, driving the young ones into the middle and then cutting them up.

Dobbs records that the corncrake was lost to Nottinghamshire as a breeding species by 1935, five years after Lawrence's death and three years after Whitaker's.

It was 92 years before the RSPB's Glen Tyler and Rhys Green were to confirm Whitaker's prescient hunch. Despite cutting in a more predictable pattern than the itinerant gangs of scythe-mowers of earlier decades, machines had one devastating characteristic: the outside-in pattern of mowing a field whose impact Whitaker had noticed.[21] Tyler, Green and Co. Dublin-based Catherine Casey investigated the behaviour of corncrakes during hay and silage mowing in the Hebrides, where there were still sufficient corncrakes to allow their study. By tracking radio-tagged females with broods and observing what happened, they found that except in the case of very young chicks, corncrakes were found to move away from mowers far and fast enough to avoid being overtaken, provided that an escape route to a refuge area was available.

When meadows were mown from the outside inwards, chicks stayed in the isolated plot of unmown grass until the last swaths fell, when 55% were killed. Mowing from the centre of the meadow outwards was found to reduce chick mortality because chicks are able to escape to unmown cover outside the meadow without leaving the shelter of tall grass.

This was just one of several consequences of mechanisation that in combination were to bring about the near-extirpation of the species from Britain and Ireland. Faster cutting by one or two people meant that it could be done earlier in the year, bringing haymaking forward into the period when corncrakes were often still sitting on eggs or when the young were very tiny. Eventually mechanisation led to a grassland revolution: the adoption almost everywhere of silage making, with several cuts a year of lush green grass. The retired farmer and lifelong conservationist Mike Shrubb has suggested[22] that the impact of silage on corncrakes is overstated, as the species had disappeared from many areas long before silage became prevalent. However, it is certainly one of the main causes of the virtual elimination of insect-rich hay meadows from the British rural landscape, leaving remote the prospect of recolonisation by corncrakes.

I reached for Jeffrey Wheatley's *Birds of Surrey*, a hefty and attractive volume which, although written as recently as 2008 gives a comprehensive summary of each species' historical status. The corncrake is recorded as common in the county until the late 19th century. A decrease had begun in the 1890s, and as noted in Yorkshire, it was on the higher ground, the North Downs, where the species persisted longest, until 1934. The last breeding record for Surrey was in 1946; the nest was robbed.

Andrew Self's 2014 *Birds of London* is another modern work that gives a historical overview. In the first years of the Victorian era it was found around Hampton and in the Woolwich area. In the 1890s they were in Harlesden and

Harrow, but in 1896 they were recorded as declining in the Lower Brent Valley. In urban areas (which in this era of mass horse-drawn transport would have had hay meadows in the remaining undeveloped parts) as well as more rural districts of greater London, the greatest decline of the corncrake seems to have occurred in the first two decades of the 20th century. After 1926 the records are again sparse enough to be listed individually, including an unexpected breeding record at Cuffley in Hertfordshire in the late 1960s.

With each volume I consulted, the story was the same, county after county. The only variation was in the dates on which the decline first became evident: in essence, the corncrake contracted from the south and east, its range shrinking northwards, westwards, and upwards in altitude.

The rapid demise of one of rural Britain's most widely-known denizens was being noticed almost everywhere. In the three or four years before the outbreak of the Great War, rising political tension on the European stage was palpable even to ordinary folk, who were also beginning to feel the effects of agrarian change. Against this background, the loss of one of the defining sounds of the summer countryside was engendering what was probably the first example of a national conservation alarm. In 1913 and 1914 Horace Gundry Alexander conducted an inquiry[23] into the status of the land-rail, as he called it, across Britain and Ireland. The results were published with urgency in the then newly-established and now venerable institution that is the monthly magazine *British Birds*. Alexander's inquiry gathered information from more than 200 correspondents. With very few exceptions, they all reported the same thing: a serious decline in the corncrake had taken place over the previous ten or twenty years.[24] In Jerome K. Jerome's Thames

Valley none was found, the species having been common there twenty years earlier. Alexander concludes that "in England, throughout the south and east .... The Land-Rail can no longer be regarded as a regular breeding species", and that "in south Wales, the west of England and all the Midlands, to the foot of the Pennines and the Yorkshire Moors, a fairly general decrease, apparently of more recent origin, is still taking place." In the Pennines and the far north west of England, however, the corncrake was described as "still very abundant", as it was in northern and western districts of Scotland and the north and west of Ireland.

Popular concern over the plight of the corncrake was short-lived: by World War II a generation had grown up never having felt warm night air vibrant with their ratcheting. Grandparents' recollections of the bird that once kept them awake, or lulled them to sleep, night after night, were as quaint and old-worldly as their fond remembrance of favourite horses, their tales from the village fair, and their songs from the field. Grandchildren lapped them up or tolerated them, passed half-remembered versions on, until they faded from the collective memory like worn-out pencil sketches.

It was for the scattered family of amateur ornithologists to keep their version of folk memory alive. The demise of the corncrake coincided with the early years of popular birdwatching. The semi-competitive nature of this pastime may explain why birdwatchers were keen to share and compare records: first dates for new summer arrivals were assiduously noted; local and national rarities might end up shot to corroborate the record; rare nesters were voluntarily protected as much for the enjoyment of hobbyists as for their own sake.

The decline of the corncrake could be charted with more precision than any other species of the era. A second corncrake inquiry was carried out in 1938–39, during which the organiser, C.A. Norris, examined 1800 questionnaires and 1400 letters from participants across Britain and Ireland.[25] The wealth of information that emerged was enough to tempt him to venture a prediction:

> If the present increase in agricultural efficiency is maintained and particularly if the policy of early mowing is pursued in the more remote areas, then the species will in all probability be reduced in status to that of a rarity in the major part of the British Isles…. In the extreme north and west of Scotland and Ireland where, for reasons of climate, the hay harvest must always be much later than elsewhere, the species may be expected to hold its own for many years to come, provided other conditions remain unchanged.

This proved to be exactly correct. By the 1990s, it had been saved from total extirpation by the colder, windier and often saltier environment of the far north west of Scotland, the Inner and Outer Hebrides, and Orkney; the Shannon Callows and Donegal in the Republic of Ireland and Fermanagh in Northern Ireland. But isolation is itself a threat, and the Shannon birds would eventually die out, as the Northern Irish population did in 1994.[26] Corncrakes were lost as a regular breeding bird from most of the Scottish mainland and Orkney by 2005. There had been none breeding in England or Wales, apart from rare and unpredictable odd records, for decades.

Further assessments came in 1978–79, 1988 and 1993 showing that from just 700–746 singing males in 1978–79, the population declined further, to 551–596 in 1988 and 480 in 1993.

I was Head of the RSPB's European Programme for much of the period during which the research carried out by Rhys Green and his associates was beginning to point to possible solutions. Similar declines in corncrake numbers had occurred in other parts of the birds' range, and Rhys started to compare notes with scientists from other countries. The corncrake was one of 24 European species under real threat of global extinction,[27] and in 1990 I was asked by the Council of Europe and the European Commission to chair a joint programme that in the course of three years brought 400 scientists together, to agree and plan the actions that would be needed to save them.[28] Rhys and a young Bavarian scientist, Norbert Schäffer, led the corncrake group. Norbert was later to move to the UK to join my team at the RSPB, taking over from me in 1999 when I moved to Yorkshire to become the RSPB's Director for Northern England.

The survival and possible return of the corncrake depended entirely on farmers and crofters. We needed to test management and harvesting techniques that would be corncrake-friendly but agriculturally viable: it is a bird of the farmed landscape, and could not survive confined to small pockets for much longer. One of Rhys's research findings was that corncrakes are short-lived birds, putting all their energies into raising two large broods each year, and rarely surviving to breed for a second season. To maintain the population an average of 4.5 chicks needed to survive to adulthood each year for every breeding female. There were clear signs that while the remnant population may breed successfully in the best areas, each year a proportion were attracted to nest in apparently suitable habitat, only to be destroyed when the fields were cut too soon, in what conservationists call the 'sink effect'. Techniques were developed, refined and demonstrated on RSPB nature reserves on the islands of Coll, Tiree and Colonsay and extended with the voluntary support of neighbouring crofters and farmers. Once the RSPB was confident they had found the right formula, the Scottish Corncrake Conservation Programme was ready for launching in 1991.

Initially, it involved the RSPB approaching farmers who had corncrakes on their land and offering conservation payments in return for them delaying the hay harvest. This would allow time for two clutches of eggs to hatch and for the chicks to grow large enough to improve their chances of escape. Special mowing methods also provided escape routes to safe refuges nearby. Farmers were encouraged to establish ungrazed areas that corncrakes could use before the grass had grown in spring and again in late summer after the grass was mown.

But RSPB funds could not stretch to cover all potential corncrake areas, so the programme included lobbying for government payment schemes to be made available at a larger scale. By 1998, most of the grassland managed for corncrakes in Scotland was being funded by EU-sourced agri-environment schemes, and corncrake numbers more than doubled. However, 2014 proved the high point in the species' recent history. 1,289 calling males were recorded in Scotland between May and July, more than at any time for at least 45 years. Since then numbers have fallen back: the 2017 survey revealed that they were at their lowest level since 2003, with just 866 calling males. Hopes of a continued recovery leading to recolonisation of the mainland were dealt a blow.

Scottish Government data show that over the same period there was a substantial decrease in the extent of land managed for corncrakes under agri-environment schemes. Take-up of such schemes have long been subject to periodic lurches between the end of one scheme and its successor. Much of the decline in corncrake payments can be attributed to one such period of shifting priorities, delayed payments and general uncertainty. It lasted two seasons: 2014 and 2015, between the end of the Scottish Rural Development Programme Rural Priorities Scheme and the start of the Agri-environment and Climate Scheme. In some areas, farmers found the new scheme less attractive anyway: the Scottish Government had decided unilaterally to reduce the payment rate for late cutting.

The corncrake story so far, then, is of a species that benefited from the clearance for settled agriculture of the primeval forests of post Ice Age Europe. A bird of naturally marginal habitats like machair grassland became common, widespread and commensal with us and our farming, and must have remained so for over a thousand years. For roughly a hundred years between about 1860 and 1960 we greeted its disappearance despairingly; a loss that would register within the living memories of a generation, before fading from the collective memory of all. It became the first and most symbolic non-human victim of the industrialisation of agriculture, and as such, part of the price of progress viewed with the same resigned acceptance as the smog of heavy industry. It had been lost from most of Britain for decades when the next lurch forward in agricultural intensification began, in response to the food security scare of World War II. The Common Agricultural Policy took the idea of post-war food self-sufficiency and created a distorted fantasy land of industrial fields and chemical soils based on an ever-tightening web of policies, each designed to mitigate the unintended consequences of the last. Eventually, a suite of such remedial schemes included some aimed at restoring wildlife to pockets of farmland from which it had been eliminated, and maintaining it where it could still be found. Agri-environment schemes have hardly been a resounding success, however, as the toll of species grows still longer.

In the 1980s amateur ornithologists were responsible for taking conservation in a new direction entirely. By then, the culture of sharing information had evolved into a systematic gathering of standardised data. Amateurs contributed their records with enthusiasm, as they still do, to scientifically rigorous surveys, to be processed and analysed by the professional scientists of the British Trust for Ornithology and the RSPB. By 1970 the scale, consistency and quality of annual survey data had reached a level where the status of almost any moderately widespread and common species could be monitored accurately, and trends recognised quickly. 1970 became Year Zero: when all species were given a population index of 100 and since then all lines on the graph radiate out, up or down from that point.

In 1983, when I began working for the RSPB, the appeal of wildlife conservation was still largely an abstract one: you might never see a red panda, a white-tailed eagle or a blue whale, but it was hoped you'd care enough to lend your support to organisations that were working for them on your behalf. My enthusiasm had been sparked by stories of the return of the avocet and the osprey, which were enough to give a glimmer of hope for the red kite and the corncrake. Then, as we watched the lines on the graph, like cracks in an eggshell, radiating from that single point representing 1970, patterns started to emerge. Plotted species by species, some lines were dropping precipitately, others less sharply, some were stable, and some rising. No real surprise there, but once the data were amalgamated into groups, two things stood out: the number of species in decline far outweighed the number increasing; and birds associated with farmland were decreasing fastest of all, much faster than the underlying trend for birds as a whole. This, too, was unsurprising, but it confirmed and quantified the concerns being expressed by birdwatchers and even by callers to the RSPB's enquiries desk. One person might worry that they were losing their skylarks, another that the song thrush no longer sang in their garden. A single yellowhammer territory may fall silent. Thanks to what we now call citizen science, such losses could be shown to be not merely local blips, but part of an alarming trend. Coloured lines were all it took to show that the relationship between farming and conservation was dysfunctional.

This changed everything. Suddenly, in the 1980s, conservation became less esoteric. If the decline of the skylark and the song thrush were not enough to universalise conservation, the later addition of the house sparrow and the starling to the danger list surely would be. These were *your* sparrows, *your* starlings, with messages about *your* environment.

The corncrake story shows us that solutions to the farmland bird crisis are there to be found. The cirl bunting was another species that seemed to be draining away from Britain, as if England's south-west peninsula were the funnel through which they were disappearing from across the southern half of England, across which they once ranged. The 'corncrake formula' of intensive research to understand exactly what the buntings needed but could no longer enjoy, experimentation to see if local gains could be made, rolling out solutions to other participating farms, and establishing payment schemes to encourage the often minor changes that were needed for the species to recover, was applied. It worked. From a low point in 1989 when just 119 pairs survived, all of them in south Devon, Britain's cirl buntings reached the milestone of 1000 pairs in 2016, enough to provide a source of captive-bred birds for reintroduction into Cornwall, where there are now over 50 pairs.

Corncrakes and cirl buntings became so rare and threatened that any small-scale success from highly targeted measures was bound to make the graph leap upwards. The greater challenge is to make wide swathes of farmland hospitable once more to the species that may still be widespread and even relatively common, but which are declining fast. These are everyone's birds, the birds we associate with our childhoods, the ones we celebrate in anthologies, the birds that provide the soundtrack to our lives: lapwing, corn bunting, linnet, skylark, starling, kestrel, yellowhammer.

Turtle dove. Only two per cent of the 1970 population remains, making it the fastest declining of all British birds. The tragedy of this most beloved of summer sound-makers is its double jeopardy. It has the misfortune to belong to two disadvantaged classes, being both a farmland bird and a long-distance migrant. The next corncrake.

THREE

Fox

We had had no rain at The Hamlet between 2 May and 13 July, and then it was no more than a token shower to interrupt a drought that was to last until late August. Lower Laithe Croft, one of two one-acre fields we had acquired in the spring, was baked hard along the snaking length of the pathway I had mown through the hay. Off the path its standing grass, already dry again after the shower, crackled under the morning sun, the only grass for miles around to have been spared an early mow. Two weeks before, as the field next to ours was being cut, above the swirling, stinging grass-dust a red kite drifted in. It had read a signal in the dust from afar, and came for the voles that were fleeing the cut. I saw it stall, twist, fold and drop, but I didn't see its parabolic swoop onto its prey; the final manoeuvre took place over the brow of a slight rise in the field, and the bird disappeared into the dust.

The grass in Upper and Lower Laithe Croft would have been cut that day, too, had we not bought the two fields from our neighbour a few weeks earlier, and decided to experiment, keeping the grass standing through the summer, beyond the July cut that would be normal for these parts; keeping half standing until autumn, well beyond the late August cut that is usually advocated for conservation-grade hay-meadows. A little of it is to stand uncut for two years, maybe three, in the hope and expectation that insects will thrive and harvest mice return.

Flower-rich meadows were only ever an accidental by-product of haymaking. With 97% lost since the 1930s, the restoration of a few became a conservation imperative, and often it is the hay that is the by-product, available to offset the costs of managing grasslands this way, or to supplement the income of farmers who accept subsidies for delaying their cut and for eschewing inorganic fertilisers. That any haymaking exists at all is thanks in large part to our continued affection for the horse, whose conservative tastes do not extend to silage or processed fodder. In this part of Yorkshire, horses are widely kept, and hay meadows cover perhaps a quarter of the farmland within a five-mile radius of The Hamlet. In a typical year, our neighbour would mow the hay in July. Some years a flock of sheep were brought in after the cut, once the late summer rain had spurred the grass into new growth. They would stay until lambing time, when they would go again, into the hills west of Huddersfield via some bright green in-by fields where they would drop their lambs and stay with them a few weeks. In other years our other neighbour's Charolais cattle would come when the grass was high enough again. They would stay for a few weeks only, and the grass would spend the rest of the autumn recovering.

My mown path rises over a rough hump of grassed-over stones where a drystone wall has collapsed. From there, the top edge of the lower field, the path descends a gentle slope through the meadow, about thirty yards in from the left-hand field boundary, which is formed by a fenced-off railway bank clothed in small oak trees. The north-bound train passes five minutes before the south-bound, giving us peace for 55 minutes out of every 60; they are slow and quiet, and we often hardly notice them at all. From the top of the lower field its far edge is hidden from view in a dip of ground but is traced by a line of trees running perpendicular to the railway, at the lowest point in the dip. From the south-east corner of our fields the trees thicken suddenly to form a 7-acre wood, which I call Wood Nook Wood, after the other hamlet that is tucked into it, across the fields from ours. From there the land rises up to the village of Upper Cumberworth, whose church steeple we can see through the trees in the wintertime, and on the slope between there and Wood Nook, there is the spring of a small stream.

1220 yards from its source, the stream runs into a culvert under the railway line. For the last 83 yards before it disappears, the two-to-six foot wide stream forms our eastern boundary, the far edge of Lower Laithe Croft; the remaining 113 miles of its course I have explored at my desk. It will acquire a succession of names on its eight-mile journey to join the River Colne at Dalton: Shepley Dike, Thunder Bridge Dike, Fenay Beck; from Dalton it will flow another 1.8 miles into the Calder at Bradley, east of Huddersfield. From there its waters will mingle with the Calder for 28 miles and flow into the Aire at Castleford. The Aire has another 31 miles to flow to its *myn*, or mouth, at the River Ouse by the village of Airmyn; 14 miles farther downstream is the confluence of the Ouse and the Trent at Trent Falls. The two rivers form the Humber Estuary, discharging 62,500 gallons of water every second, driving a final 38 miles to the North Sea, including perhaps a gallon from our stream.

When two young foxes appeared at the end of the path, having run in from the right along another mown strip that skirts the bottom edge of the field, for a second I continued walking towards them, as they turned left and started to trot uphill towards me. Then all three of us stopped, having realised our respective errors. Theirs was to see me as some new curiosity in the landscape, worth a closer look. The lead fox approached to within twenty yards, the other held back, then both shot back down the slope, turned right, back along the lower path, and were lost to sight behind the tall hay. My mistake was to recognise the lead fox – Harlequin by name – and for a moment to imagine we knew each other well. By that time she was about 18 weeks old; I had known her for 9 weeks and watched her grow to overtake her mother, a small vixen called Gadwall. But in that first second of recognition I had forgotten that I knew her far better than she knew me. Almost all my hours of observation had taken place at a computer screen, studying footage from a trail camera that used infra-red light to film life in the meadow after dark. Like bumping into a television personality in the street, you greet them as a friend, feeling foolish when you remember that they don't know you from Adam.

I crouched. Unable to see over the hay, I couldn't tell whether the foxes were still in the field, or had crossed into the neighbour's field, or run up the far side of our meadow and up the slope behind me. I didn't have to wait long: they came back, running along the lower path. As they reached the junction with my path, one cub continued across, disappearing among the oaks on the railway bank. The other, Harlequin, came up the slope towards me again, but only for a moment, before her courage deserted her and she followed her companion into the trees.

We had set eyes on each other a few times before. Her mother's den was on the other side of the railway, in an inaccessible wooded area. I would always cast a glance along the track whenever I walked across the humped stone footbridge; there was usually little to see, but years ago I caught a fortuitous glimpse of a small fox cub and it has conditioned me to try my luck every time. With its slight elevation over the land on either side it makes a good lookout for a few minutes' scan of the nearby horse paddocks, and farther to the north east, the pastureland that rises in four stone-bordered field-widths up to the top road, and the patches of oakwood that punctuate the panorama. A little owl family had their nest in an oak at the far edge of the paddock; the nest-hole was on the other side of the trunk, but occasionally the view from the bridge had embossed within it a diminutive figure on a fence-post, scanning the ground for beetles. As summer progressed, with the nights drawn fully out, the chance of an encounter with a fox increased.[1]

On 1 June, at 8.30 in the evening, Jane and I stood on the bridge looking south east and moments later Gadwall appeared below us, trotting out from under the bridge and away along the left-hand rail of the track, apparently unchallenged by its narrowness and shininess. As she made her way along the track in the direction of Denby Dale, she appeared not to have noticed Jane and me on the bridge. She was carrying something. From behind, as she receded farther along the line, I could see the limp limbs of an animal dangling either side of her head. A rabbit, maybe two.

I could tell it was Gadwall despite not seeing the face pattern for which I named her. When I first started capturing night-time footage in monochrome of foxes and badgers in the meadow, I slowly realised I could tell them apart by the shapes of their tails. To remember which was which, and to accord them due respect, rather than give them impersonal identities according to some neutral code, I named them. Smooth-tail, Double-kink, Slight-kink, Short-tail, and Droop-tail were among the names I gave the first foxes to visit in the months after I started night filming in December 2013. Then, as the seasons changed, I noticed that their tails changed in appearance, as they moulted their thick winter pelts and thinned out for summer. As the weeks passed, I got them all confused, thinking new foxes had arrived, or mistaking a new fox for an old, slimmed-down friend. Some foxes I had named for other features that did not change with the season, and those I could identify consistently. I had grown accustomed to seeing animals whose eyes shone like headlamps, but No-shine was a beautiful large fox whose eyes did not reflect the camera's infra-red light. He must have lacked the *tapitum lucidum* that many nocturnal and deep-sea animals have for retroreflecting light so that it passes twice through the receptors in the retina. He was so healthy-looking that he appeared unhandicapped: perhaps his *tapitum* reflected visible wavelengths but not IR. Maybe he had adapted his habits to hunt mainly by day. The fox I named Cut-ear had had the top third of his right ear sliced off, or so I thought. It was several days before I noticed that it was intact, but folded forward by 90 degrees. Three-paw was a small dog fox who walked and ran on three feet, using the stump of his right hind leg occasionally to steady himself as he fed. The poor chap had, I guess, been caught in a snare somewhere, and I prefer not to imagine how he made his escape. With the outlawing of hunting with hounds, snaring is the last, or at least the worst, bastion of institutionalised, legal, government-approved animal cruelty. If you want to kill a fox in the most horrible way, there is a DEFRA[3] leaflet available to tell you how.

It was Gadwall's smoky-chocolate back and tail, and paler patches on her haunches either side of the base of her tail that enabled me to recognise her as she trotted away along the rail. Once she was about 80 yards away, I said something to Jane that I thought would be inaudible to Gadwall, and immediately she stopped and looked back, noticing us for the first time. She seemed to judge that we were too far away to pose a threat, and didn't run into cover as a rural fox would usually do at any closer range, but merely switched to the right-hand rail and carried on. Then I noticed, 50 yards farther along the track, a cub, who I knew would have been between eleven and twelve weeks old. When Gadwall arrived at where the cub was waiting, she turned left, crossed the track and disappeared into the inaccessible wood, followed by her cub.

A minute later the cub reappeared at the trackside, and at that moment I heard the 2034 north-bound train approaching. To my relief, the cub did, too, and ran back into the woods. I knew that if the south-bound train was on time it would pass along the same single track within the next five minutes, the two trains having passed each other at the dual section of track up the line at Shepley station. The cub reappeared, and crossed the track from left to right. From behind me, I could hear the train approaching from Shepley; again, the cub did, too. It turned back, stepped onto the track and stopped, looking towards the sound of the approaching train. The train emerged from under the bridge, and the slight rightward curve of the track afforded me a view of the cub until moments before the train reached it. I had to watch, to know the animal's fate, and I readied myself for a stomach-churning tragedy. Then, almost casually, the cub stepped across the track to the left and back into the wood. As the drone of the train receded, I noticed for the first time the sound of the bells being practiced at Shelley church a mile away, and of a blackbird's evensong echoing off the sandstone of The Hamlet.

The next evening at 8.20 we stood on the bridge again and looked south east. The track appeared deserted but within a minute three foxes appeared from the left about 60 yards away. I recognised Gadwall; the other two were clearly cubs – smaller, less pointy-faced, less angular all together. When they saw us, Gadwall calmly led the cubs back into the trackside vegetation, emerging into the paddock on the other side. Along the far end of the paddock is a drystone wall enclosing raised ground, the former spoil heap from the cutting of the railway in 1849, now the inaccessible wood where the foxes lived. Gadwall walked along the ground at the base of the wall, while the cubs walked along the top of it. Half-way along, where it has partly collapsed, they dropped down and disappeared into the wood, their mother stepping through the gap to join them.

Gadwall had looked me squarely in the face before she led her cubs off the line and into the wood. Through binoculars I could see her muzzle pattern clearly: a blackish spot on either side, an inch back from her nose, and a bright white patch next to it. In infra-red light the pattern stands out, and reminded me of the black and white squares on the wings of a gadwall, a once uncommon duck that during my lifetime has become an everyday sight on any large stretch of water in winter. The two cubs were so different in appearance from one another, and from their mother, that as I watched them make their way along the wall, I made a note in my head, and wrote it down as soon as I had pen and paper to hand.

One cub – grey/brown back, black belly. Other – golden red all over.

They were born sometime between 8 and 19 March, between when I last saw a heavily pregnant Gadwall and her next visit to the feeding area, when she was clearly lactating. New-born foxes cannot survive long without their mother's warmth, so they would have been born close to the earlier date. Their

78

father, perhaps with the help of a related female, would have kept Gadwall fed in those first ten days or so.

Within a short time of starting to observe foxes and badgers at night, downloading each night's film onto my computer next day,[3] I discovered three things. The more you get to know a fox, even in the limited circumstances of visits to a feeding area, the more you first recognise them not by the pattern of their coats, but by personality. Their bearing, approach, gait, curiosity, nervousness, their sociability or wariness with other foxes, their comfort or otherwise alongside specific other individuals, even the patterns they describe as they move across the ground with their own personal foraging style. Secondly, they are short-lived animals. I confirmed this from the literature only after noticing that some of my favourites, those I would know on sight before they had even fully emerged from the darkness into the pool of infra-red, might not be around for more than one full year. The average life expectancy of a fox once it has reached independence is less than two years. Thirdly, while at any given time there would be a local vixen and her family; or earlier in the year a dog and vixen pair, who could be thought of as the owners of the territory, there were always other foxes around. They might be near neighbours, close relatives, wanderers, returning exiles, chancers, migrants in transit; they might appear once only, or stay a few days or many weeks. Without radio tracking and DNA analysis it is impossible to know the complexities of fox societies and clans, if such words are at all appropriate.

By 14 July and my close encounter with Harlequin and the other cub in the meadow, I would have recognised her anywhere. She acquired her name eight days before, on the morning of 6 July, as I was watching the previous night's footage. It had been a night of particularly complex comings and goings, and I had resorted to pausing the action and sketching the animals, trying to work out how many there were, and who was who. Even in the feature-stealing infra-red light, as a half-grown fox she had become a handsome animal unlike any I had seen before. I knew she was the black-bellied cub I had seen on the railway line a month earlier, and at certain angles her back showed a grey, slightly grizzled tone. Her tail was thick, smooth, dark and grizzled above, black-looking below, with a particularly large and well-defined white tip. The boundary between her black underparts, including the underside of her tail, and her grey-flecked brown upperparts was sharp, and this pattern of contrasting shapes suggested a name – Harlequin. Having named one cub, I reviewed the footage again and decided the other would be called Dot. Most of the foxes I have watched over the years have had some distinct combination of dark, blackish spots and teardrop or chevron-like shapes on the muzzle. A few, in infra-red at least, seem lacking in any such facial features save the odd white line (as with White-cheek, the likely father of the cubs) or small dark spot, as with newly-named Dot.

The following evening, from the bridge I watched as Harlequin crossed the horse paddock from one corner, where the inaccessible wood meets the railway, to the opposite corner on my left. She made her way calmly and slowly at a distance of about 80 yards from me, stopping two or three times to look up at me on the bridge. Her harlequin pattern, seen in its natural colour, was like a military uniform, russet-red flecked silver above, face red and white, and – unusually – black under her chin and belly, and along the underside of her tail, which otherwise was thick with grey guard hairs and sporting a bold white tip.

There was, in fact, a third cub. The three made their first appearances before the camera in stages: Harlequin first, with Gadwall on 8 May; I next saw her on 20th with Gadwall and the pale cub, Dot. It was another six days before the third cub appeared, with its mother and two siblings. Throughout the summer, once they had begun venturing without their mother, whether via the camera or in the flesh, I found the third cub, who came to be called Spot-smudge, to be the most elusive. Spot-smudge and Harlequin seemed to develop an early rivalry; while Spot-smudge would dominate Harlequin in their petty squabbles, it was he who became the loner. It was not until the evening of 3 August that I saw him with my own eyes from the bridge. He was foraging beyond the paddock on the far side of the railway line, and beyond the inaccessible wood. I watched from about 300 yards as he sniffed about the grass, which was washed green again from the meagre rain and infrequent drizzles of the previous two weeks. He found something, dead and feathered, and carried it away into the wood.

In the autumn Harlequin left the area, but must have moved to a territory not far away, as she made occasional but ever rarer appearances before the camera. I had not seen her for exactly a month when, on February 22, she reappeared, heavily pregnant. Until that happy moment, I believed her to be male. Her brother Spot-smudge stayed around through the winter and into spring. A new vixen had arrived in the autumn, easily identified by small black patches on her hind ankles, hence 'Blankles'. She gave birth to Spot-smudge's cubs on 9 March. I last saw Dot for sure on the day I first saw Blankles – 18 November.[4]

The history of our relationship with the fox is as hard to fathom as the animal itself. In *The Long Spring* I wrote that "for one so ubiquitous in folk stories, myths and reality, it is a difficult animal to know" and that "unlike the wolf and the bear, who instilled fear and acquired enemy status, foxes have always been treated as cohabiters, sometimes unwelcome, but animals we have had to come to terms with as they move among us"; and that "no folk depiction, ancient or modern, contributes much to our understanding of this uncanny beast."

In Britain, there arose an extraordinarily ritualised way of chasing down and killing foxes, arcane and Druidic.

> Fair was the dawn, for the hoar-frost clung;
> In ruddy red mist arose the sun,
> And the heavens were clear of clouds.
> At the woodland edge men unleashed their hounds
> And with blasting horns made forest rocks resound.
> Dogs dropped on the scent to where the fox he lay,
> Winding from side to side as is their strategy.
> A hound spoke, the huntsmen holloa'd
> The snorting pack joined force and followed.
> The fox scampered on and when they found him
> They pursued him fast with much loud shouting;
> He twisted and turned through many a grove,
> Or hid and waited in hedges to move.
> At last by a ditch he leapt out of a spinney,
> Stole round the edge of the copse so slily
> And so from the wood escaped the hounds.[5]

The poem continues as the fox is sighted again, whereupon he doubles back into the woods. The hounds gather once more, their din deafening, the clamour of the huntsmen adding to the noise. As they close in on their quarry, the fox doubles back yet again, leading the hunters over hills and into valleys. Back at the Master Huntsman's castle, a knight sleeps soundly.

This tale, vivid and suggestive of the unknown author's first-hand experience, was written in about 1380. The sleeping knight was Sir Gawain, who missed the New Year hunt as he rested. While his host, Sir Bercilak, was chasing the fox, Gawain, alone in the house with Lady Bercilak enjoyed his own sport. Their mutual seduction is described in terms strikingly similar to the fox hunt. It was their third such tryst, each following from a hunting scene, and each characterised by different manoeuvres that echoed the differing techniques of the deer-hunt, the boar-hunt and the fox-hunt.

Hunting foxes with hounds had been practiced for at least a hundred years by then: Edward I kept a pack, at a time when kings and great aristocrats were the few people with both the right and the retinue. But within sixty years, a generation before Gawain was penned, the Black Death had wiped out at least a third of Europe's people, hastening the end of feudalism in England. The changing social order was to affect every aspect of life, even the chase. A new cooperative style of hunting that was to persist into the 21st century is said to have begun in Norfolk, in 1534, when a group of farmers joined forces in setting their dogs upon a fox that frequented the local farmyards. Within a few decades, controlling fox numbers had become a secondary concern, as hunting became a social pursuit, with rules, rites, and once again a heavily stratified social order. By Elizabeth I's reign several landowners were actively preserving fox numbers for the hunt. Both she and her father Henry VIII were advised that foxes could be eliminated from the land, as lynx, bears and all but a few wolves had been, if only the gentry would allow it. In 1591 the Elizabethan soldier Sir Thomas Cockayne, veteran of the Siege of Leith, wrote an instructional treatise:

> You must breed foureteene or fifteene couple of small Kibble hounds[6], lowe and swift, and two couple of Terriars, which you may enter in one yeare, by this rule following.

You must borowe one couple of old Foxe hounds of
some Gentleman, or Yoman, who vseth to hunt the
Foxe: and when your hounds bee full twelue moneth
and a quarter olde, and that your Huntsman hath
chastized them surely from sheepe, then may you
take your seruants with you, and goe to some Couert,
where you heare there is a litter of Foxe Cubbes;
where stopping all the holes, sauing two or three,
which must be set with Foxe pursenets, to take a yong
Cubbe, to make your Terriars withall. Then must you
cast off your couple of old Hounds to finde the Cubs,
which being found, you must cast off all your whelpes
to them foorth of the cooples, and foresee that none
of them haue hunted either the Hare or Conie before.

By that time you haue killed halfe a skore Cubbes in
this sorte in seuerall Couerts or Woods, and haue
taken two or three quicke Cubbes to make your
Terriars withall, you will finde your Hounds well and
perfect.

This order of entring your whelps should be begun a
fortnight or three weekes before Bartholmew day, and
continued vntill the feast of All Saints.

The growth in recreational hunting was to lead to an
ambivalence that has characterised attitudes to the fox ever
since. In areas where the hunt had yet to take hold, villagers
seeking to control foxes would assemble at the edges of copses,
nets strung out to catch any animal driven out by their dogs.
The foxes, seen purely as vermin, would be dispatched swiftly.
Conversely, in hunting areas, new coverts were planted to

ensure there was enough habitat for a ready supply of foxes, which were left unmolested until the hunt, apart from those cubs that were used in the brutal autumn training regime described by Cockayne, and which remained part of the hunting calendar until the ban at the turn of this century. Separated from any food-related purpose, it existed for its own sake, and as a liturgy for reinforcing social strata, replete with etiquette and ritual and more than a faint echo of Paganism:

The congregation was divided into Huntsmen, Masters, Members, Followers and Servants; the vestments rigorously codified according to rank, function, season and sex. The calendar was divided into the pre-season, the cubbing season and the full hunt,[7] with high days such as the Opening Meet and Boxing Day. A rite of passage known as 'blooding' was established, allegedly by James I, but echoing the *blót* ritual of pagan Norsemen: children witnessing their first kill would have the blood of the fox smeared onto their faces. The cries, the calls and the carnyx; the courtesies and decorum; the lexis; the libation; the rules of equine grooming; the taboos; the symbolism; the invocations...

The Tudor Vermin Acts remained in force, and throughout the eighteenth century and the first decades of the nineteenth parishes paid out bounties on each dog, vixen or cub fox presented to them, the females attracting the highest headage rates.[8] But more and more land was given over to shooting, and estates employed gamekeepers to control the predators who competed with them for their quarry, with the fox high on the unwanted list. Eventually the bounty system died out as the professionals took over. In parts of eastern Scotland and East Anglia, the fox was largely eliminated, yet during the same period, many new hunts were founded, based on estates where fox cover was carefully maintained and an orthodoxy of fox management established. But this was not enough to produce sufficient foxes to satisfy demand in parts of southern and eastern England. A cross-channel trade in foxes opened up, and thrived during the century leading up to the First World War. DNA analysis has shown that foxes in southern England are today more closely related to continental animals than they are to those in the North.

The twentieth century exposed the equivocation and hypocrisy surrounding our relationship with the fox. Across the country as a whole fox numbers grew as keepering declined during and after the two World Wars, and also due to cruel but efficient killing methods such as gin traps, self-locking snares and gas being progressively outlawed. By the end of the century foxes became familiar in towns, with the rise in fast food outlets and food littering, and in due course, an increase in deliberate feeding to attract foxes into suburban gardens.

Meanwhile in rural areas game-bird shooting has become increasingly commercial. Competition between shoots has ratcheted up the 'bags' on offer – to 500 birds a day in some cases. To achieve this, estates have taken a prophylactic approach to predator control, with total war waged on crows, foxes, stoats and weasels, and, away from the gaze of the law, raptors, ravens, badgers and pine martens. In grouse country, even the mountain hare is culled by the tens of thousands; not as a competitor, but as the innocent co-host of the *Ixodes* tick, the primary vector of the virus that causes the grouse disease known as louping-ill.

Paradoxically, fox numbers in lowland rural areas are sustained by the very pheasant shoots of which the animal is their nemesis. Fifty million non-native pheasants are released every July from the pens where they spend their first eight weeks of life. Millions of inexperienced and unparented juveniles are killed on roads in the hours, days and weeks that follow, nourishing a growing population of crows and buzzards.[9] These are then shot to prevent them depredating next year's stock of poults; the crows legally, the buzzards either illegally, or with quietly-issued government licences. The surviving pheasants are shot for sport, creating an over-supply of pheasant meat that outstrips demand many times over. The carcasses may be dumped in stink pits – designed to lure foxes to their deaths by snare – but there are too many even for this, so thousands are simply stuffed under hedgerows. The main beneficiaries of this glut are the hated crows and foxes. The cycle of killing is unending.

Nazi Germany banned fox hunting in 1934, and after World War Two a return to democracy and civilised politics in that country did not see the prohibition repealed; nor did hunting return to all the countries occupied by Germany, where the ban had also applied. In the UK the post-war Labour government appointed a committee of inquiry to investigate all forms of hunting, which somehow concluded that "fox hunting makes a very important contribution to the control of foxes and involves less cruelty than most other methods of controlling them. It should, therefore, be allowed to continue."

The twists and turns of post-war hunting politics makes the story of Sir Bercilak's hunt read like an allegorical foretelling of a time to come, as reformers chase their elusive quarry through the thickets and swamps of Parliament; plodding at first, with occasional glimpses of something emerging from the undergrowth.

The chase broke into a gallop in the run-up to the General Election of May 1997, when the Labour Party manifesto promised a free vote in Parliament on the subject. The hitherto comfortable and somnambulant field sports lobby realised that it needed to employ a professionalism and a ruthlessness in its campaigning, as public opinion and the political landscape had decisively shifted against them. Within two months of the new government's arrival the Countryside Alliance was formed through the amalgamation of the British Field Sports Society, the Countryside Business Group and the Countryside Movement.

Its first move was to adopt vocabulary designed to portray rural populations as under siege from an uncomprehending urban majority: terms like *prejudice*, *coercion*, *spite*, *bigoted politics*, *blatant abuse of the democratic process*, and *unwanted political intrusion* appearing routinely in their literature and press statements. To counter opinion polls that overwhelmingly showed a majority of the British public in favour of a ban, they called upon rural people to vote with their feet and march on London. The Liberty and Livelihood March took place on 22 September 2002 with 400,000 in attendance. As pro-ban campaigners and politicians repeatedly invoked the polls, the pro-hunt side rallied the physical presence of what they described as 'real people' and invoked the civil liberties of the minority.

The next six years witnessed a breathless to-ing and fro-ing in which the thorny tangles of the British Parliamentary system snagged first one side, then the other. However in Scotland, the (then) newly established Parliament, which had been given jurisdiction over environmental and animal welfare matters, had already given the ban an easier ride. A private members' bill tabled by Labour MSP Mike Watson in 1999 took three years to become law, although pro-hunt campaigners immediately took court action to overturn it. They lost, and the Court of Session cleared the way for the introduction of the Scottish ban on 1 August 2002.

With the Commons majority resolute in its intention to ban hunting, the Countryside Alliance galloped audaciously up onto the anti-hunting side's high ground – public opinion. With the help of the ever-willing *Daily Telegraph*, they commissioned their own surveys, the results of which they then interpreted freely to confect pro-hunt conclusions. The questions included classic tricks deemed unprofessional by the market research industry: when asked which method of fox control inflicted most cruelty, 27% said "snaring, shooting or trapping" and 25% said hunting with dogs. Respondents were not given a choice between, for example, the generally efficient and humane shooting and the barbaric snaring.

"59% of the population back hunting foxes with hounds", the Countryside Alliance claimed via the *Telegraph* in 2004. The figure quickly found its way onto car stickers and billboards; and onto the desk of the Advertising Standards Authority who ruled that it was a misuse of poll results that had shown that 18% agreed hunting should continue as a civil liberty, and 41% said that some form of regulated hunting should be allowed. The poll was attacked by the Market Research Society for failing to ask objective questions, for failing to carry out research objectively and in accordance with established scientific principles, and for being guilty of conduct that might bring discredit on the market research profession. The Alliance responded by noting that the ASA had jurisdiction only over paid-for advertising, and it would ignore the ruling with regard to bill-boards placed voluntarily on private land.

With the government tiring, it sought any short cut home, invoking the Parliament Act to override opposition to a ban in the House of Lords. The Act is intended to give the elected House of Commons the final say over the unelected Lords when the two Houses are locked in stalemate. It was passed in 1911, revised in 1949, and at the time of the Hunting Act, had been used only six times before. In November 2004 the legislation passed into law and received royal assent.

The Countryside Alliance stayed true to its promise to fight the ban 'in every court in the land' and failed every time. They finally invoked European Human Rights legislation, supporting a huntsman who was seeking a ruling that the hunting community be seen as an ethnic group. The Court did not share the view proposed "that hunting amounts to a particular lifestyle which is so inextricably linked to the identity of those who practise it that to impose a ban on hunting would be to jeopardise the very essence of their identity."[10]

In mediaeval times, riding far from home and into dense forest in midwinter would have seemed a reckless endeavour for the pursuit of a mere fox. The risk, or the fear, of an encounter with a bear, wolf or murderer would have made nonsense of such an enterprise. And then … there was *Herlaþing*.

The *Anglo-Saxon Chronicle* records an event that took place in 1127:

> …after February 6 many people both saw and heard a whole pack of huntsmen in full cry. They straddled black horses and black bucks while their hounds were pitch black with staring hideous eyes. This was seen in the very deer park of Peterborough town, and in all the woods stretching from that same spot as far as Stamford. All through the night monks heard them sounding and winding their horns. Reliable witnesses who kept watch in the night declared that there might well have been twenty or even thirty of them in this wild tantivy as near as they could tell.

It is one of innumerable accounts of the Wild Hunt, of some meteorological or astronomical or hallucinatory apparition commonly spoken of in Germanic lands. The desolate silence of the night, when broken suddenly by baying winds and galloping storms, struck terror into folk still half-pagan in their fears and beliefs.

As the Gawain story tells us, foxes were third-order quarry as long as there were boar and especially stags available and men and hounds enough to rally each other's courage. American anthropologist James Howe[11] has suggested (twenty years before hunting with hounds was banned) that with the demise of nobler quarry, the English huntsman has accepted what he calls symbolic second best, because its limited grandeur is "vastly preferable to the indignities of third best. When the encroachments of urbanism break up the land too much to allow a pack to follow foxes wherever they lead, some hunts resort to drag-hunting, following a line of scent artificially laid down across the land still open to them. There is very little nobility to be gained galloping across country in pursuit of a bag of concentrated fox urine." Which is, of course, the legal form of hunting now practiced: the urine is available from specialist suppliers, and is preferred over other equally effective trail scents, as long as adherents cling to faith in a hunting Parousia.

FOUR

Badger

It was November. I had been away from home for a few weeks and was keen to catch up on the latest news from The Hamlet's foxes and badgers. By now I had learnt that autumn is a time of great change for both species. For the foxes, it is the peak of the breeding season. Pairs are forming or being renewed; young animals are finding mates for the first time; the autumn night becomes the backdrop for strange joiks and wails. For the badgers, it is the start of a long period during which their ventures above ground are fewer and longer between.

I had been passively filming badgers with the help of infra-red trail cameras for five years. They were the original reason for buying the equipment: during the first fifteen years living at The Hamlet, I had often seen clues that they were around, but I hardly ever saw them. Upper Laithe Croft, the field that was eventually to become ours, was separated from our garden by a dry-stone wall which had lost some stones over the years and was several inches lower in one corner. On the field side, there was also a line of barbed wire, long disused and dark red-brown with rust and weathering. I longed to get over into the field to remove it, at least from along the few feet of lowered wall, for there were clear signs that badgers crossed under the top wire and into the garden at that point. Claw-marks appeared, like runes freshly scratched into the green algal coating on the gritstone. In summer the algae would regrow over the scratches over a few days, and new ones would appear before long. Tufts of pied guard-hair would appear, caught in the twists of wire. I removed the hairs each time, so that I could know that the next time some appeared, it indicated another incursion, a small but welcome sign from our mysterious neighbours.

In December 2013, on the very first night, my new camera captured a still photo of a badger and a few more of a fox. I was lucky: over that winter, badger 'sightings' were few, but foxes came by every night. I switched the camera to video mode and bought a second one, and gradually a limited view of the world after dark was revealed. At least, something of the world of the fox was revealed: I came to know a little of their individual personalities. Over the years I worked out who was related to whom, which dog and vixen were paired, who lived on the manor and who would call in or pass through. But passively observing badgers as they entered a few square metres of infra-red light to feed revealed almost nothing. Their markings were not so distinctive as to make telling one from another very easy. Telling them apart by behaviour and personality seemed almost impossible. They came, usually alone, they snuffled around, they ate, they scent-marked by thumping their bums firmly into the grass, they left.

In six years, and with hundreds of 'sightings', I could list the most eventful encounters in a short paragraph: the occasional appearance of both a fox and a badger, often peacefully feeding alongside one another, or the fox slightly wary. Now and then a badger would half-chase a fox for a short distance, barely breaking into a fast trot. The arrival one night of a father, mother and small cub, and their rough play, the mother separating the male and the cub by squeezing between them as all three pirouetted about one another. Badgers sporting weeping bites on their rumps, soon to heal, characteristic of the short, soon-forgotten fights between males. Once, a badger limping badly with an injured right hind leg; I could never be sure if the injury had cleared up after a few days, or the animal had stopped coming.

I decided to invest in a thermal imager. This is essentially a monocular that detects differences in heat emanating from adjacent objects and creates a digital image that you view in real time, as if through a telescope. The hotter the object relative to its surroundings, the brighter it appears. Now I could roam to look for animals in the dark, and not have to wait until the following day to find out what a static camera might have recorded at a fixed location during the night. On a cold night (with therefore a greater contrast between a warm-blooded animal and the surrounding air), I could watch a mouse at a hundred yards, a rabbit at three times the distance and a cow over a mile away. Badgers' eyesight is poor, and their hearing only moderately good. I had the advantage, as long as I kept quiet and stayed downwind.[1]

I had an idea where I thought the badgers' sett would be, based on tracks worn into the grass and crops, that tended to radiate out from an area to which I had no direct access.[2] On 1 January 2019 at about 8pm I walked a few hundred yards from home and soon detected a large, bright shape in the viewer. There was also a vaguer brightness in some of the surrounding vegetation: where an animal had recently lain, leaving behind a short-lived glow of warmth. The badger was running, chased by another. Then it turned and became the chaser. They were no more than twenty-five yards away, and were oblivious of me. They disappeared, and I scanned the area. Soon I could see, with the help of the imager, holes in the ground that glowed warm from within. I had found the sett, in a tree-covered area just beyond the field boundary. Suddenly there were four badgers above ground, boistering through the ground cover. I could hear them clearly, but away from the viewfinder, they were invisible. I moved to the hedge line at the opposite edge of the field, fixed the imager onto a tripod, and watched.

The sett was tucked into a dip in the ground, and therefore not visible from my vantage point, but I could see the glow of its warmth, and behind it, on a bank, the four badgers again rushed into view before disappearing. They must have recently emerged for the night and were indulging in their customary pre-shift jinks, no doubt an essential nightly routine in which their social norms were re-established before the real business of the night got underway. Presently, a large, lone badger appeared on my side of the dip, where I knew there was a wire fence between it and me. The wires did not show clearly in the viewer, but it was clear that he was crossing under the fence as he flattened his body and slipped into the grassy margin at the edge of the field. Then, immediately, he began scraping at the vegetation with his front paws, gathering dry grass and wood-sage and compressing it into a bundle under his belly. As he walked backwards towards the fence, he collected more vegetation, adding it to the bundle, and eventually returned under the fence in reverse with a substantial supply of bedding. I had been watching my badgers remotely for six years, yet learned more in just over half an hour on one midwinter's night than in all previous encounters. I had confirmed the location of the sett, established that it housed at least four adults, and witnessed a domestic routine normally kept private from prying human eyes.

On 24 November 1918, my aunts Ena and Hilda, aged six and four, lost their mother. Martha Rose, my grandfather Arthur's first wife, died aged thirty-two in the so-called Spanish 'flu pandemic that killed a quarter of a million people in Britain and 50 million worldwide. Martha was not killed directly by the 'flu; in common with many other victims, the immediate cause was Phthisis, an old name for tuberculosis. It is likely that then, as now, one in four people in the world were infected by *Mycobacterium tuberculosis* or its close relative *M. bovis*, bovine tuberculosis (bTB), but most – around 95% – remain healthy, never suffering symptoms. Weakened by the most aggressive influenza strain ever encountered, though, in 1918 thousands succumbed.

Martha lived on a farm and may have contracted the bovine form: in England and Wales, between 1912 and 1937, some 65,000 people died after consuming tuberculosis-infected milk. A century on, clinical disease from *M. tuberculosis* infection is now rare in Britain, and in humans the bovine form of TB, with or without symptoms, has been virtually eliminated since wide-scale milk pasteurisation was introduced in the 1930s. Infected cattle similarly display symptoms only rarely and most live normal lives until their scheduled slaughter; unless they have undergone a test for the disease, in which case they are labelled 'responders', animals with no sign of illness but apparently infected. They are then slaughtered in accordance with a TB eradication strategy that from its inception in the 1950s until the late 1970s, saw the incidence of infection over most of Britain drop to negligible levels.

In 1971 a population of badgers was discovered in Gloucestershire, some of whom carried the bovine tuberculosis infection. Some farmers responded by culling badgers using hydrogen cyanide gas; the animals had no legal protection, and therefore no statutory basis for ensuring that any killing was proportionate in scale, humane and safe. Conservation groups had been campaigning for legal protection for decades, and there was now an urgent need to bring the matter under control, for the animals' sakes and to avert a public health mishap. The Badgers Act 1973 and later the Protection of Badgers Act 1992 made it an offence to attempt to kill, take or injure badgers or to interfere with their setts without a licence. A licencing scheme was duly set up.

Bovine TB had been contained in isolated pockets, but after licenced badger killing was scaled down in the 1980s it started to spread, covering parts of the west and south-west of England and Wales. The main farmers' organisations attributed this to a reduction in badger control, and in 1998 the government set up the Randomised Badger Culling Trial[3] (RBCT) to ascertain whether the apparent connection was real. The trial was scheduled to be carried out over ten years and was to be overseen by an independent scientific group, or ISG.

In the event, the trial was closed two years early because it was manifestly counter-productive. John Bourne, Chair of the ISG, stated: "badger culling can make no meaningful contribution to cattle TB control in Britain. Indeed, some policies under consideration are likely to make matters worse rather than better". He made clear the panel's finding that "the rising incidence of disease can be reversed, and geographical spread contained, by the rigid application of cattle-based control measures alone." The trial demonstrated first-hand that disrupting the badgers' highly developed social order resulted in TB being spread more widely – the so-called 'perturbation effect'.

Far from settling the matter, the scientists' findings proved merely an early stage in a war of words that continues to rage unabated thirteen years on, stoked from the outset by the government's own Chief Scientific Advisor. Professor Sir David King, a world-renowned physical chemist, took the unprecedented step of issuing a report of his own. He concluded that despite the ISG's findings culling should nevertheless take place as having a useful contribution to make to controlling bTB. This surprise move shocked the scientific establishment, whose unofficial mouthpiece, the journal *Nature* responded with an editorial[4] under the headline *A government that asks for independent scientific advice had best be ready to take it*. The article criticised "the mishandling of the issue by David King" as "an example to governments of how not deal with such advice".

Trevor Lawson of the Badger Trust pointed out that "Professor King's list of recommendations repeat virtually word for word the opinions of farming unions." The then deputy president of the National Farmers' Union, Meurig Raymond, took his cue not from the ISG report but from Professor King: "Now we have scientific endorsement for the principle of badger culling, there can be no further excuse for the government not to act."

It gave the government licence to initiate, in August 2013, a pilot of what it called 'science-led culling in the worst affected areas', starting with parts of Gloucestershire (including nearby parts of Herefordshire) and Somerset, with the target of killing 70% of the badger population in the areas concerned. When that proved unachievable, Environment Secretary Owen Paterson reduced the target to 60% for the following year, stating, against the evidence of his own government's trials, that this would "deliver clear disease benefits as part of a four-year cull." He did, however, cancel plans for the pilot to be extended to another ten areas, when the Independent Expert Group set up to oversee the pilots reported that they had been neither effective nor humane. In 2014 the cull teams failed to reach the much-reduced target by a considerable margin.

With science relegated to a footnote in the debate, the fate of badgers was firmly in the hands of politicians, and at the mercy of political judgements alone. The broad-scale cull that Paterson had abandoned was reinstated by his successor, Liz Truss, who saw no need for scientific advice and disbanded the Independent Expert Group. The government changed the way cull targets were calculated, replacing fieldwork and DNA testing to gain an accurate estimate of local populations, with desk-based extrapolations of theoretical statistics. Prof. Rosie Woodroffe, a badger expert who worked on the RBCT, described the approach as "rubbish science" designed to make the targets "unbelievably easy". By 2018 the cull was taking place in 32 zones across eight counties and would see 32,601 badgers killed that year.

*

Badger culling proven to reduce bTB in cattle, new research shows, claimed a National Farmers' Union press release in October 2019. *Badger cull makes TB worse*, ran a headline in the *Guardian* two months later.

Two statements that cannot both be true, and that sum up the political stalemate in which farmer and badger alike are trapped. The first referred to a paper[5] by Sara Downs of the Department of Epidemiological Sciences, part of the government's Animal and Plant Health Agency. Dr. Downs was careful not to draw the conclusion from her study that the NFU reads into it; indeed, she describes her results as reasonably consistent with the RBCT, given the range of natural annual variation in TB rates in cattle. As the number of years and the number of areas studied were quite small, the results would be particularly sensitive to that variation. Rosie Woodroffe pointed out that in Gloucestershire, which appeared to show the biggest effect of badger culling, there had been an increase in TB in cattle in 2019, the year after the study finished, "so it is possible that if they were to repeat the same analysis, the benefits for [that year] would not look the same as they do in the published study."

In the second study, Cally Ham from the Zoological Society of London tracked the movement of 67 badgers across 20 cattle farms in Cornwall, in areas with and without culling.[6] She found that as soon as culling began, badgers roamed over an area of land 61% larger than those living in zones without culling. They also visited 45% more fields. This confirmed and quantified the perturbation effect found in the randomised trials of 1998–2006. Cattle are thought to get TB principally from bacteria left in their fields by infected badgers and the increased movement caused by culling could spread the disease and create new sources of infection lasting for several months, long after individual badgers have been culled.

However, Stuart Roberts of the NFU repeated that the science "definitively shows the phenomenal impact culling badgers has on reducing TB levels in cattle".

For years the government and the National Farmers' Union on one side, and conservationists, animal welfare activists and ecological scientists on the other, have exchanged fire across clear battle lines. Traditional enmity towards animals labelled as vermin, which are met with the traditional response of lethal control; or a search for a compassion- and tolerance-based solution involving vaccination and more disciplined livestock management. It was also a battle between evidential rigour and anecdote, between evidence and opinion. In England, where the UK Government sets wildlife and farming policy, Conservative Party ministers had clearly come down on the side of the traditional view and their traditional farming constituency, and presented their interpretation of the evidence accordingly.[7]

Following another study, this one commissioned by the government itself, a group of vets accused the government of telling 'bare-faced lies' after farm minister (later promoted as Environment, Food and Rural Affairs Minister) George Eustace claimed that the cull was successful in bringing down bTB rates in cattle, when there was compelling evidence that the cull was largely ineffective, often counter-productive, and hugely expensive. The government-commissioned report[8] in fact suggested that the main cause of continued bTB infection in cattle was the poor take-up of on-farm biosecurity measures and that widespread trading in high-risk cattle was severely hampering disease control. Iain McGill, a vet and former government scientist who had helped expose the Bovine Spongiform Encephalopathy scandal[9] of the 1980s and 90s, and was now coordinating a group of fellow vets, researchers and campaign groups opposed to the culls, was scathing.

"The entire paper relies on data which is two years out of date without even considering subsequent data available for 2018, which saw a 130% increase in confirmed bovine TB cases in Gloucestershire, as well as a doubling of the incidence rate", he said. "Using 2018 data, it is clear that there has been an overall worsening of the burden of disease in both Gloucestershire and Dorset since culling first began.

"Using 2017 figures to justify continuing this cull, when the government's own 2018 data shows just how disastrous it has really been, is like choosing to report only on the first half of a football match just because it doesn't suit you that the final score was a bitter defeat." McGill based his assessment on government data[10] that had been quietly released hours ahead of the announcement of plans for the 2019 cull: a further expansion, with a target of 60,000 badgers to be killed that autumn.

"DEFRA have manipulated and hidden scientific data to such a degree that it amounts to systematic scientific fraud," he said.

Badgers were apparently uncommon at the end of the 19th century. In East Anglia, 1,450 social groups had been exterminated by gamekeepers in Norfolk and Suffolk, where only 150 groups remained as late as the 1980s.[11] In other areas, badgers were dug out alive by men who would pit them against specially-bred dogs and would place bets on which animal would finish the encounter alive. Badger-baiting was outlawed in 1835 but the animal itself was not legally protected from other forms of persecution or disturbance until 1973, by which time badgers were becoming more common in south-west and central England, and central and north Wales, but remained unrecorded in parts of East Anglia and northern Scotland.[12] In the following decade, badgers recolonised some of the areas they had disappeared from and a population estimate was made, suggesting a total of 250,000 badgers living in Great Britain, but with gaps remaining in London, East Anglia, Lincolnshire, Lancashire, and northern Scotland. When the first pilot culls were being planned, in 2013, there were an estimated 485,000 badgers in England and Wales.[13,14] In the part of Yorkshire where I live, in the metropolitan borough that now goes by the name of Kirklees,[15] there are 704 known badger setts, an average of 4.5 per square mile. Each is mapped precisely and many of them are regularly inspected by volunteers.

There are two fronts in the battle to protect the most ancient of Britons, and while the threat of a pre-emptive cull against bTB appears to be receding, the greater struggle here is against the scourge of badger-baiting, 185 years after it was declared illegal. I joined the Kirklees Badger Protection Group, attending their monthly evening meetings as often as I can. The meetings are held in a small back room of the bowling club in the village of Brockholes, whose name is derived from the Old English *Brocc-hol*, badger sett. Across the road, The Rock Inn has the sign of the badger swinging from its wall.

Sue Shaw has presided over the group's meetings since 2005, working through the agenda with a quiet, methodical delivery that is almost child-like in timbre. But behind the voice and the cascades of auburn curls is a steely personality, essential for the role. The meetings follow a standard pattern of reports on the group's activities over the previous month which, depending on the season, might be some combination of sett inspections, artificial sett construction, analysis of 'RTAs' – road traffic accidents – to gain detailed demographic data, or providing advice to planners and developers, as well as generally spreading the word and fundraising. The meetings usually end with reports passed on by the local police wildlife liaison officer, PC Caroline Newsome, or from members themselves, of recent incidents of note. It can be a hard listen: the meeting of 17 October 2019 was typical.

We learned that ten days earlier a Dewsbury man, Anthony Oakes, was banned from keeping dogs for two years after five of his animals were found with serious injuries. He had pleaded guilty to offences under section 4 of the Animal Welfare Act 2006, namely that he caused unnecessary suffering to the dogs in failing to have the injuries treated. Police, acting on a tip-off, had raided a property the previous February and found his five Patterdale terriers with serious damage consistent with their having been fighting with badgers. One of the dogs had to have an eye removed after an infection went untreated. In addition to the ban, magistrates fined Oakes £500 and ordered him to complete 200 hours of community service. Oakes did not face charges relating to how the dogs had come by their injuries: proving an offence under any of the legislation that protects badgers, or forbids cruel sports, is difficult enough even when witnesses come forward, as another case the same month showed.

An incident within walking distance of The Hamlet was tried on 14 October. The accused was charged with interfering with a badger sett and with causing unnecessary suffering to an animal. A witness had seen him with his head inside the sett entrance and called the police. Two police officers arrived quickly and caught the man still interfering with the sett. He was cautioned and his mobile phone taken for analysis: it was found to contain graphic footage of both cock fighting and dog fighting.

His defence team included names well-known to the group, and familiar as the two Stephens who had defended Oakes the previous week. Stephen Lomax is a qualified vet and barrister, who has appeared for hunts, terriermen and gamekeepers in courts across the country and as an expert defence witness in cases involving badgers. He is a founder member of Vets for Hunting, now known as the Veterinary Association for Wildlife Management. Stephen Welford is a solicitor in wide demand as a Countryside Alliance favourite whose cases have included both successful and unsuccessful defences of huntsmen accused of illegally killing foxes and successful and unsuccessful defences of others accused of violence towards hunt monitors.

Lomax used the same simple argument that had helped him secure acquittals in numerous similar cases. Although, as an 'expert witness' his role is to give unbiassed information, as a witness called by the defence team, they would be relying on his views supporting the defence case. The offence of disturbing a badger sett applies only to active setts and there is ample room for debate as to what 'active' means. Lomax argued that the sett was not known to be active at the time of the alleged offence, despite the Court being shown film footage of a badger entering the hole two weeks later. While his credentials as a badger expert are unclear, he is an expert at casting doubt on whether a sett is active simply by stating a contrary view, knowing that harder evidence that would contradict him had not been obtained in good time by the prosecution. The Kirklees case in October 2019 failed for exactly this reason.

To the glum assembly at the Brockholes Bowling Club, a group member who had attended the case made an observation that yielded little comfort.

"There are a lot of learning points to feed back to the police from this case."

The romantic figure of that anonymous rustic folk hero the mediaeval poacher must owe something of his allure to his dogs, the mere possession of which represented an open flouting of authority. For four and a half centuries, for a labouring man to own a lurcher, or any hunting dog, let alone hunt with them, was unlawful. Then over four years in the 1830s, the legal relationship between man and dog changed completely. Firstly, in 1831 the game laws were repealed, lifting the class-based restrictions on hunting. In 1835 the Cruelty to Animals Act outlawed pitched fighting between animals, from cock-fighting to the baiting of bulls, bears or badgers with dogs. There was nothing unlawful in owning a bulldog or a bull terrier, as long as the main purpose for the breeds' existence – to fight – was not served.

The lurcher's association with clandestine brutality has never gone away. It is linked in the popular mind with hare coursing, now illegal, and thence to fox hunting. But many are the enthusiasts for the breed itself, in its own right as a family dog, a large animal with a reputation for being safe and friendly among children. Lurchers have been bred for centuries as the perfect poacher's dog, combining the speed of a longdog with the intelligence and trainability of a working dog. Then at some point in the early 21st century, a new breed began to be traded: the bull lurcher. Crossing a pit bull terrier with a lurcher produces an animal of great speed and stamina that works hard at the command of its owner and is possessed of a vice-like jaw and an unmatched instinct to fight. It is a slavering hell-dog with two purposes to its existence: to lend to its owner a Gestapo-like status among his peers, and to rain bloody death upon Britain's most powerful native animal, the badger.

I arrived at a pub car park on a hilltop outside Huddersfield for the Badger Group's annual summer evening outing. Sue Shaw was already there, chatting to a big man in a camo jacket, who was sitting at the wheel of a mud-spattered white van. Other members arrived and we set off down a steep cobbled road. Sue introduced the man as Clive Turner from Silkstone, and explained that he had built 70 artificial setts over the years, including – six months earlier – the one we were going to see. As we turned left into a green lane that clung into the west flank of the hill, two green woodpeckers flew across the view from right to left against the backdrop of the Colne Valley and the mills and viaduct at Quarmby and Longwood. In the distance, ten miles or more away, was Emley Moor and its famous landmark TV mast, somewhere below which sits our hamlet.

I was the newest member of the Group, and the only one not to have previously met Clive. As we walked down towards our destination, he helped me understand the special and polemical place of badgers in local society.

"Industry in South and West Yorkshire has really been beneficial to badgers. Mine workins, coal measures in West and South Yorkshire, they're in what they call an *adit*, or a level. These aren't shafts, these're tunnels that run into't sides o't hills. So imagine this valley, coal measures'll outcrop onto't sides o't valley, so what they used t' do is tunnel into't side o't hill and basically make vast cave systems, an't badgers've utilised this, especially in South Yorkshire, where't coal measures're really rich. Old midden tips, Victorian bottle tips, badgers're in these. If it weren't f't quarries and mines, there'd be no badgers in this area, 'cos they can't be dug aht. One o't drift mines is 288 metres before it levels out into't old workin's and' badgers've been in that. These rock crevices and old quarries, they're really safe. But it's places like Doncaster, which is low lyin', and it's sandy soil, so't diggers get into that. It's a massive problem, badger diggin'."

We climbed a stile into Brockhall Wood,[16] where the new sett was built the previous December among the sycamore, elm and ash trees. Sue opened a scrapbook of photos of the operation and explained that the aim was to get badgers that occupy a natural sett in the lower part of the valley, and which was dug out last year, to spread up the hill and establish a larger group, including some in the digger-proof new sett.

"This is a great site because it's public – a lot o' dog walkers come in 'ere. Badgers are tucked away, it's always an advantage to have somewhere not too depopulated. Everybody up 'ere keeps an eye on it," she said.

"Because it's a really low badger population up this end, because o't geology," said Clive. "I mean it's straight into rock, so we've used a machine, and what we want is to basically mek a breedin' earth so that they can produce cubs and these cubs'll reinforce other areas. If they get into a small pocket, wi' no new blood comin' in, like in Doncaster, they'll die out, this is a good way to bridge populations."

We arrived at the new sett and Sue dropped onto all fours at the entrance hole, a 12" pipe within a low, stone revetment. She switched on a small, bright torch and immediately found something caught in the rough stone edging.

"You see owt, Sue?" Clive asked. "That's an 'air – oooh! Lovely!" The group crowded round.

"She's found an 'air... it's definitely been visited. Brilliant."

"How far back does it go?" Group member Isobel asked. Clive pointed to a low ridge up the slope, about thirty yards away.

"Right up there, there's two big chambers, concrete boxes filled with beddin' and there's an area badgers can continue to dig. Idea wi' this is, if you put a dog in 'ere, the two chambers are right up there, they interconnect to each other wi' pipes, but't badgers can dig on, they can dig further in if they want.

"Because there's so sparse a population up here it'll take a while for them to get into it, but we've looked after't drainage, it's all secure, so if anyone puts a dog in, and tries to dig it 'ere, there's conveyor beltin' over it, which can't be cut, and then there's about a thousand quid's worth o' mesh, all overlapped, so they can't physically dig it. A badger'll not bolt from this, they've got to listen to't dog, barkin' underground. They'll dig it, but they won't get through."

"So is there a natural sett around here then?" I asked.

"There's two the other side of the field, one was dug [i.e. dug into for badger-baiting] last year," Sue replied. Farther down the slope, through the trees beyond the edge of the wood, I could see a 10-acre field shimmering in the green-gold light of the evening. "We've known of this wood for about fifteen years and there's never been badgers in it. We asked the group that manage the wood if they'd be interested in us putting a sett in and they were really keen. It's a nice place isn't it?"

As we returned uphill to our cars Clive told me more about his work. "I've carried out 400 different badger projects – artificial setts, badger protections. It's took forty years. We've 'ad one farmer in forty years who said 'no'. People get on about farmers bein' negative, they're not. They get a bad press, farmers, but they say 'yeah, yeah, you can protect it'. They don't want people diggin' 'em. Obviously they're worried about TB, but they're OK with what we're doin'. We just 'ad one refusal, an' that was a guy who let people dig. But't majority o' farmers're fine. They've got no problem wi' badgers."

We climbed the cobbled lane back up to the hilltop, arriving to the sound of a distant wicket falling somewhere down in the valley.

*

A month later I was watching the dark sky grow gradually lighter behind the squat, square tower of St. James's church, Taxal. I had left home at 3.30 in the morning to drive the 34 miles to get there, and feared I would arrive too late: three times I was diverted onto less familiar lanes by blue flashing police lights. For two weeks at the end of July, rain in that part of Derbyshire had been as bad as anyone could remember. The Todd Brook had carried it into the Toddbrook reservoir, whose dam had been protecting the 6,000 inhabitants of Whaley Bridge for 181 years. The dam was on the point of collapse, Whaley Bridge had been evacuated, and the race was on to pump the reservoir down to below the faultline.

Somehow, I found my way to the rendezvous point and arrived a few minutes ahead of the others. Debbie Bailey of Derbyshire Wildlife Trust, her partner David, and volunteer Georgie Hutton arrived a few minutes later in a Wildlife Trust Toyota Land Cruiser and we set off together for the first of two farms, whose badgers we had come to vaccinate against bovine TB. As we drove to the first farm, Debbie, a former nurse who has been studying badgers for fourteen years and running the Trust's badger vaccination programme for the past six, explained how the programme worked.

"It takes 12 days per site. For the first three or four days we bait the area with peanuts which we place under 3–4 kg stones, which badgers can move easily enough but foxes can't. We set up trail cameras to get an idea of numbers, so that we know

110

how many traps to set and get an idea of what proportion of the social group we manage to vaccinate. We put cage traps out, with the bait inside, once the badgers have been coming for a few nights. We replenish the bait each night for a week, but don't set the traps so they can come and go until they're used to the cages. Then we finally set the traps overnight, as we did last night, so we'll have some badgers to vaccinate this morning. We'll set them again tonight, to catch any we didn't get last night, which should only be one or two, then that's it for 12 months. You've got three hours from first light to vaccinate all your badgers, that's the licence criteria."

David explained that they check the weather forecast twelve days ahead, always knowing that the prognosis is liable to change during that time.

"You can't set traps if significant rain is expected between about midnight and 4 am. Last month we set 40 traps across the area then the forecast changed at the last minute and we had to go out again and unset them all. That was the night of the Whaley Bridge downpour."

Waiting for us at the first farm was Tim Birch, the Trust's Conservation Director, and he and I walked to the far end of a 3-acre horse paddock while the others drove across to set up a mobile vaccinating clinic on the tailgate of the Toyota. When Tim and I arrived at the car Georgie and Debbie had donned facemasks and rubber gloves and were unlocking cases that contained syringes and phials. David, Tim and I walked to the edge of the field and climbed over a fence into a wooded area where five traps had been set the night before, in sheltered spots a few tens of metres apart. The two closest to the top of the wood had badgers in them – an adult and a well-grown cub, sitting surprisingly calmly, growing only slightly more agitated as Debbie and Georgie approached.

Georgie had qualified as a lay vaccinator only three weeks earlier, after an intensive three-day course, having spent the summer assisting Debbie on early morning sessions. On most days, including this day, she would then go straight to work as a lab technician for Specsavers. I could see that the pair were practiced in the operation: the badger would be manoeuvred to one end of the roomy cage with a moveable partition and held there firmly for the few seconds it took to scissor-clip some fur, inject the vaccine and spray a spot of colour onto the animal's back, thus ensuring that if it was caught the following night, it would be recognised. Then the cage was opened and the animal trotted away into the undergrowth. A few metres down the hill another cub had been caught, and was swiftly dealt with in identical fashion; the remaining two cages had not been visited.

Back at the vehicle, the needles were disposed of in a yellow sharps bin and forms filled in, recording such details as each animal's age, demeanour, respiration, body condition, any injuries and movement. As we drove to the next farm Tim explained that they were two years into the Derbyshire vaccination programme which has been funded for four years by a £300,000 government grant matched by £100,000 from the National Trust. But something was playing on his mind: a government decision that threatened to undermine all that they had achieved so far. In a bid to expand the cull still further, farmers had been invited to form local companies to undertake badger culling across wider swathes of England. Four Derbyshire farmers had formed such a company and applied for the county to be included in a list of ten new cull zones.

"The government is making its decision imminently," he said. "14 areas have formed companies and applied for ten licences between them. It would be madness to grant a licence to Derbyshire, with the country's largest and most successful vaccination programme."

We arrived at a farm in Furness Vale, where four young badgers were waiting for us in their cage traps. I watched as

Debbie and Georgie manoeuvred, clipped, jabbed and sprayed the first one. Then they opened the trap.

"Look at him," said Debbie, "relaxed or what?" as the cub looked out of the cage, rolled onto its back and yawned, before getting to its feet, walking out of the trap and trotting away. Once the two women had injected the second animal, I was given the job of spraying a blue spot of stock-marker paint on its back and watched as 'my' badger jogged along a fence line and into a thicket of rhododendrons.

The morning's work over, we repaired to Debbie's house to review the project in the context of an ever-more confused bigger picture.

"People often ask how does vaccinating badgers help cattle," Tim began, "but it's the wrong question because it suggests that badgers are causing the problem. We have to remind people that it's a cattle disease, spread by cattle, so you have to treat it as such."

"They think you have to vaccinate every single badger," said Debbie. "In fact, thirty percent of the social group vaccinated means you have 76% clan immunity; 60% vaccinated gives you 92% clan immunity. We know from camera traps that we get around 80% of the social group. I don't go round telling farmers I'm going to stop their cattle getting TB, I tell them I'll make sure their badgers are healthy, it's up to them and their neighbours – make sure everyone's biosecurity is up to scratch, keep an eye on who's slurrying where, cattle movements and so on.

"We've had a case where a farmer we've been working with had a positive test for TB. We'd vaccinated a high proportion of the badgers on his land and all the neighbouring farms. His was a closed herd, so it was really surprising. We asked him to check on his neighbours, turns out his neighbour got TB earlier on and they use the same slurry contractor. Every farm is totally different. We have a farmer who'd never had TB, then suddenly his herd gets it, he's had to have all sixty animals shot. Turns out he had a bull in on contract, the bull's TB records showed he was clear but he wasn't. The bull had to be shot, but not before he spread TB to another farm as well, so he's now suing the bull owner. We've got 56 farmers on our books and only two do everything possible to keep TB away from their cattle."

"The Government say they want to offer farms 'choice' – to offer badger culling or badger vaccination. But they're not promoting cull and vaccination equally," Tim pointed out. It costs the taxpayer on average £496.52 to kill a badger or £82 to vaccinate one. They're offering farmers the chance to form cull companies and take the cull into new areas – why not form vaccination companies?"

*

It is clear that the political goal of eradicating bTB is unachievable without a comprehensive crackdown on husbandry practice that is anything less than exemplary.

In any other area of public policy the approach would be to manage the risk rather than the hazard. Take road safety: effective risk management does not require the hazard itself to be eliminated; if it did, there would be no cars on the road. In the case of bTB the primary risk – to public health – has been minimised for over half a century. Policy has since shifted from human health to farm stock, and unrealistic expectations have been raised that complete protection is possible. Even more unrealistic is the assertion that reducing badger populations is an effective way of achieving that goal.

In 70 years of compulsory herd slaughter the commercial and psychological burden on affected farmers has been harrowing. Cattle have commercially short lives, during which even infected animals are unlikely to present clinical symptoms. It is the impact of the test-and-slaughter policy rather than the disease itself that causes the greatest disruption to farm businesses. The farmers have no control or choice in how the risk is managed, only in how compliant they are prepared to be. As DEFRA's own report states, and Derbyshire's direct experience demonstrates, this variability in compliance is severely hampering disease control. A rethink is needed.

One approach that has been suggested[17] is for the disease to be controlled primarily by vaccinating cattle. Farmers would be free to continue routine testing, for their herds to acquire 'TB-free' status; or to choose 'vaccinated' status instead, according to their commercial judgement of the market conditions or their personal preference. Any animal showing *clinical* symptoms of TB would be tested and either slaughtered, or if possible, isolated and treated. Meanwhile the national programmes of milk pasteurisation and inspection at abattoirs would continue.

On 6 September 2019 the government turned down the Derbyshire cull company application, prompting the four farmers who had applied to challenge the decision in the courts. They suggested that the Prime Minister, Boris Johnson, had been unduly influenced by animal welfare activists, of whom his fiancée Carrie Symonds is one. By early 2020, the first signs that the government might finally be rethinking its strategy had begun to appear.

Fifteen months after Prof. Sir Charles Godfray's 2018 independent review into the government's bovine TB strategy, on 5 March 2020 the government published its response, titled *Next steps for the strategy for achieving bovine tuberculosis free status for England*. It sets the goal of eradicating the disease by 2038, and accords the highest priority to accelerating field trials to make a cattle vaccine available within five years. The badger control policy will 'evolve' to increase support for badger vaccination and ultimately phase out culling. Minister George Eustace announced the response by saying that "the badger cull has led to a significant reduction in the disease as demonstrated by recent academic research and past studies. But no one wants to continue the cull of this protected species indefinitely so, once the weight of disease in wildlife has been addressed, we will accelerate other elements of our strategy including improved diagnostics and cattle vaccination to sustain the downward trajectory of the disease."

Most newspapers ran dramatic stories, talking of a seismic shift and U-turn in government thinking on badger culling, but had failed to notice Eustace's continued reliance on the "first half report" that ignored data from years that showed the cull had made matters worse. Accelerating the development of a workable cattle vaccine is welcome, as is the implication that the focus should now switch finally to the problem species – cattle. But the government's response is clear that the "current intensive culling policy would begin to be phased out in the next few years" and that "culling would remain an option where epidemiological assessment indicates that it is needed." The picture remains confused, but it seems likely that around 300,000 badgers will be killed, and that the killing will be brought to an end when the politics dictates, not the science.

FIVE

Willow tit

I don't know how *Poecile montana kleinschmidti*, the British willow tit, exercises its hold, but there is something about it that birdwatchers find inexplicably charismatic. Bull-necked, plain-clothed, rough-voiced hewer of wood; a no-bullshit plain-speaker, a rough-diamond worker. Maybe we all identify with some small detail of its person; in my case, to have retreated from the south and become a kind of northerner. It is, perhaps, the only bird whose habitat is preferentially post-industrial; and may be the only bird of near-zero renown to have had a collection of poems published in its honour. Steve Ely found his first willow tit's nest in 1979 and thirty-nine years later wrote a poem – titled *1979* – to commemorate the occasion. Along with eight others it makes up his third collection, *Zi-Zi Taah Taah Taah – The song of the willow tit*. Steve is a lifelong inhabitant of the same post-industrial landscape and an unflinching chronicler of its tight-plaited human and natural histories.

Poecile montana kleinschmidti

Latinised from the Greek, poekile, fem, nom,
sing – *piu piu piu*; 'many-coloured' [sic],
the analogical frescos of Zeno's Stoa
a 'now unidentified small bird': putative
titmouse, motley caeruleus? Poecile, a genus
within the paridae, congeners including lugubris
(the sombre), cinctus (siberian) and atricapillus,
the almost identical black-capped chickadee.

'Of the mountains' [sic], fem, declined
in agreement with the gaudy hybrid-noun,
strict canons of ICZN; the wooded slopes
of Alpine Graubünden, haunt of the type spec,
(Conrad 1827), 'coniferous forests of pine'.

Genitive, 'belonging to Kleinschmidt':
Otto, who spotted the skins in the British Museum
amid trays of pinned palustris dresseri (1897).
'Kleinschmidt's many-coloured mountain bird'

[sic], the sub-specific British race of nominate
montanus [sic] (HBW v.12, p.712), the willow tit:
in Osgoldcross, often found among willows;
at Howell Wood, down Peggy Lines, the copse
beside the ancient pack road razed by HS2.

Steve Ely 2018[1]

Our first walk together was in the summer of 2017, along
a few miles of South Yorkshire's Dearne Valley. The River
Dearne rises less than a mile and half from the source of our
stream by The Hamlet, and flows its separate eastward course
via the Don, finally joining forces with our stream in the Ouse
at Goole for their final 46 miles to the sea. The area between

Darton and its confluence with the Don at Denaby Main is designated the Dearne Valley, a kind of brand name for the pit villages whose mines closed at the end of the bitter strike of 1984–85, sending them into a generation-length decline and to the bottom (or rather top) of the UK deprivation league. The area's slow, painful recovery saw many of the old collieries, shunting yards and railway lines transformed into nature reserves. At Adwick Washlands, one of a chain of reserves in the RSPB's Dearne Valley complex, a group of us assembled in the July for a walk and poetry reading, part of the annual Ted Hughes Project festival, based around nearby Mexborough, where Hughes spent his teenage years. Steve sported the possibly unprecedented combination of proletarian round spectacles, orange apron (identifying him as one of the organisers of the walk) and high-end Swarovski bins. Early in the walk we heard the harsh, nasal *taah taah* part of a willow tit's call from deep within a thicket of goat willow. Between readings by poets Brian Lewis and Matthew Clegg, Steve and I realised we shared a fascination for this bird that has suddenly found itself playing a part in mining history. I revealed that I was part of the Back from the Brink programme, and that the willow tit was one of our target species, and Steve immediately decided he wanted to be involved.

For the following year's Ted Hughes Project walk, fifteen of us assembled at Carlton Marsh, another former coal mine turned nature reserve. We walked along a disused railway line raised above the surrounding marsh, stopping now and then to hear Steve read from his new collection. He began by introducing the willow tit, which he described as "nowadays a bird of old colliery sites, dismantled railways and canals." The willow tit has not always been associated with the remnants of lost industry, although it has always inhabited wet, wooded areas rich in insects and a supply of half-rotten tree trunks in which to excavate a nest. In recent years something has gone badly amiss, and its British population has plummeted by 94% since 1995, with a 50% contraction in its range. Steve's poems may have all been inspired by one small bird, but winding through were riffs on themes as diverse as the former coalfields' heroin problem, the evils of capitalism, and Plenty Coups, chief of the Crow nation who wore a chickadee (the North American version of the willow tit) plaited into his hair.

Unlike Carlton Marsh, the places depicted in *Zi-Zi Taah Taah Taah* are all within walking distance of Steve's home, and in late March 2019 he, Cathy the whippet, Billie the Nuttall Patterdale and I walked out from his front door in Upton and turned left along the former Hull-Barnsley railway. The old course of the railway has overgrown over the decades and is now a wood that shrouds the remains of Upton station, a ghostly platform that has become mossed and nettled in the 52 years since the last train passed. Its daffodils have gone feral. Steve explained the history of Upton succinctly: the colliery opened, closed, opened again and closed, attracting successive waves of incomers who stayed to form successive waves of unemployed. It closed for good in 1964, just 37 years after its first coal was raised. Steve grew up in neighbouring South Kirkby, and Upton was the place to which you never ventured.

We passed a 6-boughed coppice sycamore. On one roughly horizontal section of one limb Steve had nailed a rough remnant of plywood to serve as a bird table and an unknown person had provisioned it with seed that morning. There was a blue tube-metal skeleton of a McDonald's dining table among the assorted jetsam, probably removed from a skip by local youths and brought in to furnish a den.

"You often come across stashes of drinks cans and other stuff nicked from the local store. All that polythene is the shrink-wrap from bulk packs of Lucozade."

Throughout our walk through the trees and alongside the ponds of the old Upton colliery we stopped wherever Steve had previously found willow tits, and each time I took a small, black speaker out of my belt-bag to play exactly two minutes of willow tit calls and songs, before waiting for exactly two minutes to see if we had elicited a response from any willow tits present. A national willow tit survey was arranged for 2019 and 2020 by the RSPB to help determine whether the bird's status had changed since the last time any nationwide audit was made. That was in 2007–2011, for the compilation of the most recent *Atlas of Breeding and Wintering Birds of Britain and Ireland*. We were therefore following a standardised approach, to help ensure comparability across the country and over different time periods. It meant playing the same recordings that everyone else in the country used, for the same length of time. At Upton, we drew a blank.

"Last year I had at least one pair here, and I saw four together at the bird table. But I only ever saw or heard them on about one visit out of every six occasions. This year so far it's zero out of 13 or 14 visits." We emerged from the trees and crossed the new South Kirkby by-pass, named Sprockhovel Way after the town's German twin.

"This is the final link in the road to nowhere," said Steve. "I objected to it when it was first proposed in 1989 and fought to stop it. This was where you used to come to get away from traffic noise. Now at night-time it's a race track. Four youngsters were killed in 2015 when someone hit their ATV at 140 mph." Steve's poem *If You Want Blood* from *Zi-Zi-Taah Taah Taah* is dedicated to the 2.7-mile stretch of tarmac, the violence (another Steve Ely fascination) of its imposition; of its bisecting 'the last significant area of open countryside in the Upton/South Kirkby/Hemsworth area, including significant willow tit habitat'; of the noise of it; the misuse of it by racers; the roadkill; the hunting dogs in the disjointed fields and hedges alongside. The poem imagines disaster befalling the opening ceremony and introduces Plenty Coups as well as Leonard Peltier, a jailed American Indian Movement activist who killed FBI agents in a shootout. All the while 'willow tit keeps her counsel – *zi-zi taah taah taah*'.

In places the line of the old railway is raised high above the surrounding ground, and we run-shuffled down the steep bank to our left to inspect Long Plantation, a detachment of 25-year old trees. Willow tits need rotting, standing wood into which to excavate their own nest holes, creating a new one each year. In Long Plantation there were few senescent specimens, so Steve had fastened stumps of older wood to the young trees using cable ties. We played the recorded song sequence: no response. There was one stump with signs of digging – an inch-diameter depression of freshly plied-out wood, and a few shavings on the ground below. Perhaps an early-stage nest hole, or a test-dig abandoned as unsatisfactory for some reason.

Back up on the old railway towards South Kirkby, at this point marked by only a narrow line of trees and bounded on either side by arable. In the distance a man was approaching with two big dogs, a tan-coloured mastiff type mongrel and a German shepherd. The two men put their four dogs on their leads, and the man's two big ones barked at Steve's two small ones, who barked back as we passed. We looked back to see the man pulled over by his dogs; he somehow managed to throw himself over the tan-coloured one, avoiding falling on top of it.

"That was a good fall", said Steve.

"I meant to do that", said the man, like an embarrassed eight year-old.

We talked about the dog culture of the coalfields: Steve's whippet is a conscious adherence to tradition and to his personal roots in contrast to the more recent machismo-driven taste for barely controllable monster dogs. Steve had taught

English in schools in the neighbouring boroughs of Doncaster and Rotherham before being appointed deputy head and then headteacher at Darfield, Barnsley.

"The lads were all Billy Casper[2] and I got on pretty well with them. They liked me because I had whippets."

"I suppose if they're out after rabbits with their whippets they're more connected to nature than many kids these days, and on their own terms, which is how I remember it, rather than the packaged-up nature experience you get these days when you're taken to a nature reserve," I said, only half-convinced.

"With us it was bird-nesting. I had my crisis of conscience early, though, when I was about nine, so my mates and I were an odd clique at school – the nesters who didn't take eggs." In the prose-poem *1979* Steve refers to this self-imposed code. The fifth of seven paragraphs begins:

> There's no place for Tony or Dave in this story, but
> they were *definitely* there, unless I was on my own;
> Dave itching to get at it, for an egg or a young-un,
> or simply to see or handle the contents, so that it
> could *count*; he knew the rules, and was certainly
> no scagger, though he murmured against our YOC[3]
> ethos.

Steve's writing is eclectic. *Oswald's Book of Hours*, his acclaimed first collection, was hewn out of multiple seams in the Osgoldcross wapentake, to use the Danelaw-era name for this land, as Steve himself is wont to do. It is an exploration of contemporary Northern English identity disguised as a mediaeval handbook of devotions; and nature invariably finds a way in.

"I'm about to start a new project, about eels."

"Eels?"

"And burbot. And sturgeon in Germany. I've got a small grant to buy chest waders and fish tanks and to cover travel costs. It'll be a collection charting the history of eels and man. I've got a working title: *Eely*."

So far, we had heard no territorial singing, nor even seen a willow tit, and we had been checking all Steve's tied-up stumps and as many suitable-looking natural boughs as we could, looking for early signs of new excavations. Our survey had got off to a poor start, but we were heading for more promising ground at South Kirkby pit, via Blue Fish Lake, named after the painted iron sculpture at its shore.

"In 1989 this was all black coal spoil. Before restoring it after the pit closed they open-casted it to get the last few reserves. They dug the hole, then it pissed it down over the weekend and the hole filled up, so they gave up. It was supposed to be restored to farmland but we formed a group to campaign to keep it as a lake and miraculously they agreed."

At the edge of South Kirkby tip, now a dense thicket into which the roar of nearby Sprockhovel Way poured like a river burst from it banks, two willow tits seemed to have no trouble hearing the playback, and responded immediately. The dense growth made them hard to follow, so we contented ourselves with noting their presence for the official record. Then over the Sheffield-York railway line to a place Steve calls Mutton Flatts, once Mouton Flatts, a Norman field system now buried a hundred feet below the spoil tip that was deposited there during the 50s and 60s. The tip was in turn wooded-over with birch, including a stump with new willow-tit pickings. We examined it with care: the stump rocked in its footing, no doubt entering its final season as an upright.

"When I was a kid there were snipe and hares here, even though it was a working pit. I used to sit up here on the tip, when it was all black coal and watch the snipe drumming down at the foot of the tip where it was wet and boggy, with all the filthy plant driving past."

At some point the track doubled back under the Sheffield-York line close to where it crosses the Leeds-London line and I realised that we had been walking in what should have been familiar country. It was a landscape I had watched from the London-bound train two or three times a month for years, but only now was I part of it – able to hear, smell and feel it for the first time. I reached into my belt-bag for the black speaker box again, only for the willow tit recording to be interrupted by the Cross Country Edinburgh-to-Plymouth. As its din died down, the loud song of a wren filtered in, followed in turn by quieter sounds as the train receded: a blue tit in the scrub at the edge of the line, and distantly, an ice-cream van chiming, and the streets and houses of South Emsall echoing it, like a suburban folk chorus: "a-hunting we will go". For some reason the blue tit attracted more of my attention than usual. I had caught a glimpse of it, and took it for a newly-fledged juvenile, on what would have been an unprecedentedly early date. On closer inspection, it did indeed have the yellowed-over plumage of a youngster, but at the same time was as bright as an adult, with a bright green cap, back and wings. I called Steve, who had wandered thirty or forty yards away, and we agreed it was a rare xanthistic bird, one with a genetic mutation that had deposited abnormal amounts of yellow pigment in its plumage, something I had never seen before.

We followed Ea beck – pronounced Ee-a – out of South Kirkby and turned left down what Steve calls the Pack Road towards Clayton, with Howell Wood across the fields to our right. This was another familiar landscape, through its place-names at any rate, commemorated in the poem *1979* as the place where Steve found his first willow tit's nest and *'where we sneaked up on Dobber shagging Gail in the bushes'*. I started to realise that this was an autobiographical walk, and that *Zi-Zi Taah Taah Taah* was a shared autobiography – his and the bird's, ghost-written by Steve. We stopped to take in the panorama.

"This is my old nesting patch. HS2 will come through there." He gestured the proposed route of the High Speed rail line. "The epitome of London-centric vanity politics."

HS2 has been described as the biggest deforestation project since World War One, and the Woodland Trust has identified 21 ancient woods and a hundred others threatened with destruction or damage. The project is planned in three phases, the last of which, known as phase 2b, will affect Yorkshire, as well as willow tit sites in their other post-industrial strongholds in Greater Manchester. The official draft environmental statement for phase 2b anticipates damage to 12 Sites of Special Scientific Interest, as well as 111 Local Wildlife Sites and 19 ancient woodlands.[4]

I had been losing my bearings with each doubling-back of our path and each crossing and re-crossing of two railway lines that themselves cross. Walking below one railway embankment we had to wade through ankle-deep water on the path, turn right under the railway line then right again, in the reverse direction along the other side of the tracks. This took us into Frickley Country Park, the former Frickley-South Emsall Colliery, which had seen continuous production between 1905 and 1993, a relatively late closure at which point 740 men lost their jobs. These are hybrid landscapes: superficially early-stage birch woods with goat willows in the damp hollows and half-grown ash trees on the higher ground; at ground level the flora is typical brownfield, and the air mixes scents of clinker dust and mugwort. A thrash into the densely-packed trees in pursuit of a tantalising bird-call could involve walking over mossy tarmac or dodging between unidentifiable concrete structures or twisted angle-iron relics. In such a place Steve spotted a small bird flying between trees across a disused works road.

"There's one!" He had picked up on its plum-shaped silhouette before I did. A bull-necked bird, as depicted in Steve's poem *Bullhead*:

Broken to light, the jizz is undeniable; / Neanderthal
brow-ridge, chocolate brown, / bulging to the
nape. The einkorn-crunching / mandibles of the
linearbandkeramik.[5]

And another. We clicked on the playback just to make sure,
noted the details for the official record. The ice-cream van was
getting closer: "a-hunting we will go."

For 221 years the willow tit had been undercover in Britain.
Francis Willughby's *Ornithologiae Libri Tres* was published
in 1676, four years after his early death from pleurisy, by
his friend and tutor John Ray. Two years later it appeared in
English as *Three Books on Ornithology*. It was the first comprehensive bird book of the early Enlightenment, in other words
one based on fresh scientific enquiry rather than relying on
a combination of folklore, Biblical authority and classical
scholars like Aristotle. But the great work finds no place for
the willow tit. Nor, a century later, does Gilbert White appear
to be aware of the bird's existence throughout his long career
as a naturalist. It took a German, Otto Kleinschmidt, to
realise that the willow tit was indeed to be found in Britain.
He was almost certainly already familiar with the species,
at least with museum specimens, in his own country. He
would also have known the marsh tit, a bird both Willughby
and White knew well. Only with good views and careful
observation in the field could the two be separated. Both
species have black caps and whitish cheeks, brownish backs
and paler underparts, but the willow tit's frostier underparts
and greyish tint to the back and brighter white cheeks are
diagnostic... except in Britain. Both have their own distinct
British forms, with the British marsh tit a little more willow-

like, and the British willow tit a lot more marsh-like. To tell
them apart, a perfect view of their subtlest features is needed,
something the willow tit in particular rarely affords. Then it
is a matter of noting that the marsh tit has a glossy back cap,
the willow's being dull black; and that the willow tit's wing
feathers have narrow whitish edges to them, which form an
indistinct pale panel in the closed wing.

In 1897 Kleinschmidt and his Hertfordshire-based fellow
countryman Ernst Hartert examined the British Museum's
collection of marsh tit skins and found two specimens that
showed these two diagnostic features of the willow tit. Thus
the *kleinschmidti* race, and a new British species, was born. His
findings were made more widely known ten years later, when
Hartert's employer Lord Walter Rothschild published the first
detailed description in *British Birds*.[6] This led ornithologists
throughout Britain to set about re-checking local records, at the
same time gradually learning how to separate the 'new' species
from the presumed. Even today, any birdwatcher who gets a less
than perfect view, no matter how confident they are of an ID, will
hope that the bird obliges with its one unmistakeable character:
zi-zi taah taah taah, or, if it is a marsh tit, 'two quaint notes like
the whetting of a saw', as Gilbert White stylishly put it.[7]

I had my own willow tit survey patch to cover. At the far end
of Lower Laithe Croft, oak, rowan and sycamore trees grow
along the stream to mark our boundary and shield our view,
except where there is a twenty-yard gap, a window onto a
gently rising 12-acre barley field and the continuation of the
railway treeline. The barley field is bounded at the far end by
a thicket of birch known locally as the Broggs, a name that
derives from an old word referring to tenants' right to fodder
their animals on brash cut from the trees. The Broggs in turn

would block our view of the land beyond, but that it rises again, to a hill-brow at 728 feet, 112 feet above us. This brow is two-thirds of a mile away, and is mostly oaked and hollied, except for a gap where often a dozen or so Ayrshire cattle break the skyline.

In the twenty years since we moved into The Hamlet, willow tits have been uncommon enough visitors that I would make a note whenever I saw or heard one; yet frequent enough for me to suspect that there was a pair or two breeding somewhere nearby, at least in some years. Records have become sparser during that time, while the national picture shows that the rate of decline of the willow tit has been almost unprecedented, the second-steepest fall towards extirpation from Britain after the turtle dove. Several hypotheses have been put forward to account for the decline of the willow tit, including competition from other tit species, predation by great spotted woodpeckers and habitat change. In order to test these theories, in 2007 Alex Lewis and her collaborators[8] studied woods that were occupied by willow tits and paired these with woods within 50 km that had been abandoned by willow tits five or more years earlier. They found no differences in numbers of either potential competitors or potential predators between the abandoned and the occupied woods, and only one habitat difference: soil water content was higher at occupied sites. The progressive drying-out of the British countryside, and in particular its woodland, could therefore be implicated.

Its plight was of such concern that the RSPB organised a national survey, to take place over the spring seasons of 2019 and 2020, to gain as accurate a picture of its situation as possible. At the same time the Back from the Brink programme funded RSPB scientists,[9] with the help of local ecologist Geoff Carr, to carry out in-depth studies into the Dearne Valley population, looking in detail at how they use different features in their habitat and to understand their movements around the landscape. I joined a team of volunteer surveyors, and Geoff warned us that the birds can be difficult.

"We had one that was fitted with a radio transmitter," he said. "We got it with the receiver and could hear its signal getting closer. It started about 200 metres away to the south, and we knew it was coming towards us; it kept coming, and it passed us about four foot away in the bramble, and carried on past. It ended up a hundred meters in the other direction. One of the team was following it with the receiver, and I was looking for it with bins. Neither of us got even a glimpse of it."

The previous year Geoff and his team found 21 territories in the Dearne Valley, an apparent catastrophic decline from 70 in 2015. Geoff pointed out, though, that with the birds so difficult to pin down, it could simply have been due to very different weather conditions between the two surveys. 2018 saw bitterly cold winds over the survey period, with very low temperatures overnight and during the day, along with periods of heavy snow fall. Optimistically, birds may have been present but not yet ready to expend energy on setting up territories; or they could have perished in the cold weather, with the prospect of the population recovering over a few milder years. The worst scenario was that there had been a steady and rapid decline over the three years, due to possibly irreversible factors. The 2019 and 2020 surveys would be crucial in determining the mood among willow tit enthusiasts within the Dearne Valley and nationally.

There were five places within my designated patch – a 2km x 2km tetrad that included The Hamlet – which I felt could be suitable for willow tits, where there was some combination of woodland, dense scrub and wet ground. Between February and April I visited each place three times, mapping my route and marking the points, 200 metres apart, at which I stopped and played the recording. Each time I played the songs and calls for exactly two minutes and waited exactly two minutes before moving on. Only in the Broggs did I get a response, on two of the three pre-determined survey visits.

Following a standardised monitoring method in order to gather comparable information across the country was crucial for building a national picture, but left little opportunity to really get to know the bird, so as well as making my three timed and mapped survey visits, I visited the Broggs many times through the spring and summer. It is a dense patch of trees, 260 yards long and 70 yards wide, oriented north-east to south-west lengthwise. Nowhere is the ground flat, rather it is like a wooded dunescape of mounds and hollows, long-abandoned spoil heaps that had been covered in trees since at least 1854, when it appears on the first Ordnance Survey map as Brogg Wood. In high summer, standing on one of the southernmost mounds and looking north, the Broggs gives an impression of an ancient wild wood, with large oaks interspersed with mature downy birches. Holly trees and their numerous sapling offspring form a dark middle stratum which is shared by hazels, a few elders and occasional drapes of honeysuckle. On the sparse patches of ground not colonised by bramble, the grail-like husks of empty bluebell pods are scrambled over by the delicate climbing corydalis, a fumitory with spikes of tiny, off-white, green-tipped flowers.

At the beginning of the season, late March, I would look up from the same mound and see mostly sky, through birches as yet leafless but with millions of tight catkins, bunched like ack-ack smoke. You can't move silently through the Broggs, the holly scrapes at boots and bramble snags coats. I would move in short, twenty or thirty yard phases, and then stand for a long time, hoping the birds would adjust to my presence. It can take an hour and a half to travel the length of the Broggs that way, but eventually a willow tit was confiding enough that I could study the way it worked the trees. Two blue tits flitted at the outer edges of the trees, while the willow tit stuck to the middle reaches of the gnarliest birch, a diligent labourer, plying and hewing at the broken ends of twigs, working its way through the branches.

In spring the shapes, colours and sounds in the landscape change daily. Every brush-stroke on the canvas seems to be reapplied afresh; every combination of sounds is unique. On 3 April three male blackcaps had arrived and were singing fast, rich, complex polyrhythms in short, varied phrases. At the same time fifteen fieldfares were gossiping in a line of tall sycamores. Summer and winter birds overlapping in the first days of spring, although the sky had deemed it winter, and let fall a shower of icy rain. I made for the Broggs's one yew tree as the only shelter and waited it out. There was a soft brown leaf-mould underfoot. Hail turned to rain and back to heavy hail. I watched the pattern of it bouncing off the arching bluebell leaves and the leaves' reflex see-sawing in response. I listened to the weather's music: a tidal flow of heavier and lighter precipitation, and the sonic transitions between dry hail and wet sleet, with the occasional slowdown and pause as if the clouds were re-loading. The birds could remain silent for only so long, and lost patience in turn: blackbird first, singing to the slowing patter of diminishing rain, then the fieldfares resumed their chatter. A starling's glissando was like a release of pent-up pressure. From their high perches the birds could see the end of the shower before I could; and it finished later under the trees, anyway. Then, unseen, a brief confirmation that the willow tit was there – a ringing *piu-piu-piu-piu* from another part of the wood.

I measured the advance of the season by the slow clouding of the sky as buds turned to leaves and small leaves grew broad. Another ten days on there was a green-hazed *altocumulus floccus* above. Two willow tits responded instantly to a short burst of playback. One (I presumed a male) perched above me vertically, *piu-piu-piu-piu*. The other responded with a wing-shivering gesture before both birds started working the twig-breaks again, spending time together in the gnarliest birch. It was looking promising.

That was the last I saw or heard of the willow tits in the Broggs until late summer. Geoff Carr had warned us that they may go very quiet once nesting is underway, and while I had hoped to discover a nest so that I could pin their location down for more close observation, I had had no luck. I pass these woods two or three times most weeks, as my route to the RSPB office involves walking through the meadows of Upper and Lower Laithe Croft, over the stream and up the steep bank on the other side, alongside the barley field to left or right, across one or other end of the Broggs and up to the cattle farm that sits on the skyline as viewed from The Hamlet. Then down through more barley for another half-mile before a final quarter mile along the streets of Denby Dale. One morning I took the left-hand path along the barley field, following the treeline alongside the railway. I slowed down as I walked past the north-east end of the Broggs in the hope of a definitive *zi-zi taah taah taah* or the less distinctive alternative *piu-piu-piu-piu*. Their silence was half-expected, but combined with their elusiveness, would also leave a nagging doubt as to whether they had stayed to breed at all. Where the land rises beyond the Broggs to the brow of the hill, the railway disappears into a tunnel, re-emerging just before Denby Dale. My playback survey earlier in the season had revealed no willow tits in that spot, yet that morning I was sure I caught a distant, muffled snatch of *taah-taah-taah*. A few minutes of hard listening, and eventually the bird came closer. It was some performance

– a more intense and varied song than I had heard all spring. It seemed about 100 yards way, but I had no access across the line. I knew that on the other side was a former brickworks, now some kind of aggregate plant, but I had never been there. Checking Google Earth that evening, I discovered that there are two small ponds there, surrounded by what looked like a scrubby willow patch – typical willow tit habitat. Was this a second pair, separated from the Broggs by 250 yards? Or did the Broggs birds' territory extend to the old brickworks, and they had chosen to spend more of their time there?

11 May was peak bluebell time in the Broggs, and peak birdsong: great tit, mistle thrush, yellowhammer from the edge of the wood, blackbird, buzzard (calling from The Hamlet), chiffchaff, robin, wren, song thrush, blackcap, bullfinch, pheasant in the barley, willow warbler, but no willow tit. I walked to the tunnel end, and pointed the playback speaker across the railway towards the brickworks. I got an instant response, but from behind me, on my side of the track. It was in an oak that formed part of a tall, thick hedge, one of three lines of trees that enclose a small triangular barley field.

Eight days later it was there again, and I managed to watch it for a minute or two. High in the oak it found a cocoon of some kind, and I saw it tear off flakes of silk like wrapping paper, which floated away on the breeze. From twenty feet below, I could barely make out the contents, but it appeared to be filled with small eggs, like yellowish caviar. The bird claimed its prize and carried it to a neighbouring branch, where it deftly seized two caterpillars before flying into the line of mature trees that formed the northern boundary of the triangular field, and disappeared from view. I had found no nest, but had a pair on territory, one of which had carried food: 'confirmed breeding' in the jargon.

Email from Yorkshire Wildlife Trust's Sophie Pinder, 24 July 2019:

Results from this year are a bit disappointing – 26 territories in the Dearne Valley which is up from 21 last year so going in the right direction. We are pretty confident that there are more though, Geoff Carr in particular believes that some birds have become so accustomed to the playback recording that they no longer respond. There have been a few surveys now where the bird has been seen minding its own business even though the recording is being played.

HOTTEST DAY ON RECORD. By seven in the evening of 25 July, signs of normal life were returning to the trees at the bottom of Lower Laithe Croft but I still had to stand in the shade of a hawthorn to watch. First it was a flash of willow warbler in its primrose-yellow juvenile plumage, one that had had the hang of being a willow warbler for a while, and could spark out of an oak's dark interior into the fierce light and melt back with its prey in a single split-second movement. It was joined by several others, bright juveniles and burned-out adults, and by a gang of long-tailed tits. They are the gentlest rampagers, vanguards to a spree of mixed varieties, great and blue tits, a coal tit and the first willow tit of the post-breeding season.

It stayed within the outer skin of leaves, and I only saw it piecemeal: black curve of nape between sprigs of hawthorn on the first look; brown mantle in the V between overlapping oak leaves; black bib as it stretched its neck back to scope a morsel of prey on the twig above. And the whole thing once only, on a ten-foot bobbing sector of flight-path between a holly and the deep dark interior, in pursuit of the long-tails, followed in turn by the willow warblers. So I couldn't see if it was adult or *juv.*, but assumed it was one of the Broggs-Tunnel End birds, out of territory in a hot tree-top food-romp. It reminded me of Steve Ely's poem *Unsuccessful Attempt to Capture a Willow Tit.* 'Capture', perhaps, in the sense of 'describe', with finely detailed similes for the birds' plumage and appearance, like the black bib it sports under its chin: 'inky delta bleeds from beak, frays hoarfrost into throat'. And the collection's last line:

Flits in and out, goes missing for years.

SIX

Field Cricket

June 7, 1772. Field-cricket makes its shrilling noise.

June 1, 1773. Field-cricket sings: sings all night.

April 24, 1779. The field-crickets in the Short Lithe have cast their skins, are much encreased in bulk, show their wings, being now arrived at their ἡλικια.[1] 'Til this alteration they are in their pupa-state, but are alert, & eat; yet cannot chirp, nor propagate their kind.

May 23, 1784. Field-crickets cry, & shrill in the Short Lythe.

June 9, 1789. Field-Crickets shrill on the verge of the forest. Cuckoos abound there.

May 29, 1791. The race of field-crickets, which burrowed in the Short Lythe, & used to make such an agreeable, shrilling noise the summer long, seems to be extinct. The boys, I believe, found the method of probing their holes with the stalks of grasses, & so fetched them out, & destroyed them.

Gilbert White, *A Naturalist's Journal* (extracts)

It is difficult to know how widespread the field cricket was in Gilbert White's time, but it is tempting to imagine that his journal entry of May 1791 was the first sign of the impending extinction of the insect whose 'cheerful summer cry' he seemed to love. What White certainly knew – because he discovered it himself – was that field crickets have an annual life-cycle: they emerge, mature, reproduce and die within a year, with the future of the species entirely dependent on the survival over winter of dormant nymphs that hatched in the summer. So if Selborne's crickets didn't make it through the winter of 1790–91, it would indeed have been a local extinction of an insect that, having no power of flight, may never have returned to its former haunt.

The Short Lythe is a field, now owned by the National Trust, at the northern edge of the village. White described it in 1779:

> There is a steep abrupt pasture field interspersed with
> furze close to the back of this village, well known by
> the name of the Short Lithe, consisting of a rocky
> dry soil, and inclining to the afternoon sun. This spot
> abounds with the gryllus campestris, or field-cricket;
> which, though frequent in these parts, is by no means
> a common insect in many other counties.[2]

From the north east corner of the churchyard of St. Mary's, where Gilbert's grandfather Gilbert was vicar between 1681 and 1728, an old, wooden kissing gate leads out of the village via the Glebe Field. Our Gilbert, as a graduate of Oriel College Oxford, was not entitled to the living, which was in the gift of Magdalen College, but as curate, he would have had a short walk from the church to the fields where he studied his crickets. I walked the same path 240 years later. The Glebe Field drops steeply to the Oakhanger stream, and the path runs to the right of a large oak tree that Gilbert may have known as a sapling. The land to the left of the stream rises steeply and is cloaked in a hanger wood of beech and oak, to the right it is more open, and wet-flushed in places. A marsh tit called as I crossed the short, narrow footbridge at the foot of Glebe Field, and I thought of Gilbert's own description of the call: 'two quaint notes like the whetting of a saw'. I was to see or hear another six along 800 yards of the stream as it flowed along the Short and Long Lythes, two fields that today are separated only by a broken line of elders and hazels, dating to more recent times. It was a warm September morning, and a few half-spent yellow agrimony flowers, perhaps a second flush, arched over the grasses on their curving stems like rapidly-expiring fireworks. Betony and devils-bit scabious were more of the season, and lent purple and blue pointillistic touches to the scene.

Gilbert White's essay on the field cricket takes the form of a letter to his fellow naturalist Daines Barrington. It opens with the Latin words *resonant arbusta* – the heathland resounds.[3] He borrowed them from Virgil, who wrote of heaths resounding with cicadas, and for White to have chosen this fragment from the *Eclogues*[4] is telling. They are poems preoccupied with sound, and with hearing the world in a way that mediates the connection between people and nature. For both crickets and cicadas lend the air around them a kind of sonic physicality that is as vital a part of the landscape as any geological form or meteorological effect. They are nature's percussionists. Virgil's cicadas use a tymbal, a membrane under their abdomens which they flex rapidly like a microscopic thundersheet. White's crickets stridulate – running a ribbed part of one forewing over a ridge on the other, like a güiro. For Virgil, and therefore for White too, it was a sophisticated metaphor: this resonance imbued their writings with the spirit of the places in which they are set.

The song of the field cricket once resounded across the heaths and dry grasslands of Surrey, Sussex, Hampshire and the Isle of Wight, before falling silent from the summer night air everywhere, except in one last place in West Sussex, where fewer than a hundred individuals survived into the 1990s. This steady attenuation has not been limited to Britain, and in Germany, the Netherlands, Belgium, Luxembourg, Denmark and Lithuania it is officially listed as a threatened species. What these countries have in common is the great acreage of heathlands and nutrient-poor grasslands that have been fragmented, degraded and lost.

The field cricket inhabited the open commons where people would graze cattle and keep trees at bay with periodic burning. It may never have spread beyond the River Arun to the east, the Solent to the west or the North Downs to the north, and during the twentieth century, as 70% of England's heathland was lost to afforestation and housing, the field cricket disappeared from almost all of its original range. In those fragmented heaths that remained, it became impractical to pasture livestock, so the patches of short grass that the crickets require grew rank. By 1991 the field cricket was on the brink of extinction, its population declining even at its one remaining location. In that year the government agency Natural England, in its earlier guise of English Nature, worked with the Zoological Society of London's Invertebrate Conservation Centre to establish a breeding population in captivity. Meanwhile some of the crickets' former haunts had been restored back to suitable condition and over the following years captive-bred crickets were released onto seven sites in Hampshire, Surrey, West Sussex and the Isle of Wight. It was still present at four of the new sites in 2007 but had failed to establish at the other three, and one apparently stable colony suddenly dwindled to extinction through a combination of poor weather and habitat deterioration.[5]

By 2010 it was clear that larger areas of habitat were needed within a greater overall distribution to ensure a stable, resilient population. At the RSPB's Farnham Heath reserve in Surrey, a former forestry plantation nine miles from Selborne, around 240 acres of the original heathland had been restored by removing the conifers that had been planted there in 1950. This created ideal conditions for field crickets: short, warm, tussocky grass with 10–50% bare ground. As Gilbert White had recorded in the eighteenth century, the bare patches are needed for egg laying and are then used by the young nymphs. The adults develop and overwinter under grass tussocks, constructing burrows at their base and feeding on grasses and other vegetation. The reintroduction programme was extended to Farnham and by 2016 this one new population had exceeded 300 individuals, at least three times the size of the entire national population at its nadir, two decades earlier.

However, the field cricket's future was by no means assured. Two of the remaining populations were very isolated and one was very small, making them vulnerable to changes in grazing or land use and to heath fires. Half of the sites were privately owned with no guarantee that they would be maintained in suitable condition. Management there depended on agri-environmental payments to ensure appropriate grazing and bracken control continued. The UK's imminent departure from the European Union threatened to cut off this source of support. Government austerity measures were draining funds from its own Species Recovery Programme, threatening the progress of collaborative efforts involving Natural England and voluntary bodies such as the RSPB.

In 2015 I joined a team drawn from eight organisations, including Natural England,[6] to put together an ambitious funding package that would enable them to work together on species like the field cricket. We sought to break new ground by working across the range of threatened species, irrespective of each organisation's specialism. With a total of nearly £7 million funding for four years work, Back from the Brink got under way in spring 2017, comprising nineteen projects across England. With field cricket funding restored, the RSPB's senior reserves ecologist Jane Sears and Farnham Heath warden Mike Coates set out to increase the robustness of the population by translocating crickets within Farnham Heath itself.

I was keen to join them, but it being early April, we had for some weeks kept the timing of the work under review, as cold or wet weather would have made the job impossible. The appointed day dawned well, but at some point after I boarded the 1053 from Waterloo and before I caught the 1204 bus from Farnham Station, a low cloud descended and bleached all colour from the landscape. It seemed to thicken during the mile walk from the bus to the RSPB's portacabin office in the grounds of the Rural Life Centre. I diverted left across the heath, which at its western end was still mainly a forest of plantation pines; in patches there were also young birch that had launched themselves from the seedbank wherever pines had been removed during the last decade or so.

In the mist the trees appeared to be arrayed in troupes, each line successively more faded into the flat middle distance. The chill did not bode well for crickets, but failed to suppress the first willow warbler song of the year. Nor did it inhibit a male stonechat from performing a military-ceremonial display, with blazing white epaulettes and in full dress uniform. He paraded atop a small birch sapling then up into half-dry pine tree where he delivered a song, which by its scratchiness seemed itself to be a thing of the heath. And it being early April, in sheer defiance a wren hurled a song, and a blackbird curled another, into the mist.

I stopped to watch a Dartford warbler in a small silver birch. Perhaps the dim light had encouraged it out of its usual abodes deep in the heather and gorse. It was a male in full spring lust. His tail was cocked, so priapicly so, that when he leant forward to pick an insect off the farthest bud he overbalanced and tipped over and off his perch. He flew out of the fall, landing 50 yards away in another birch before disappearing into the heather.

In April 1773 a pair was shot on a common near Dartford and John Latham, a renowned ornithologist living in nearby Darenth sent the specimens to Thomas Pennant. Pennant, coincidentally, was one of two men to whom Gilbert White addressed the letters that were later compiled as *The Natural History of Selborne*. Pennant was compiling his *British Zoology*, in which he published the first description of the Dartford Warbler in 1776: '…whole of the upper part of the head, neck and back dusky brown tinged with yellow; underside of neck, the breast and belly deep ferruginous…'

As British winters have become milder, the Dartford warbler population has increased, and spread to the north as far as Derbyshire and west into Pembrokeshire. Its heartland is in Spain and southern France, and future climate-based projections indicate that by 2080, much of its southern European range may no longer be suitable.[7] The northward shift is already underway, and the Dartford warbler has declined severely in Spain and France.[8] If these trends continue, the UK may become the global stronghold of a bird endemic to a few tens of thousands of square miles of western Europe.

The RSPB Farnham Heath reserve office is an incongruous addition to the collection of vernacular and traditional buildings reassembled as an open-air museum at the Rural Life Centre.

Half a dozen volunteers and staff were already crammed into the space when I arrived, warden Mike Coates was on the phone trying to resolve some local issue, and someone gestured an offer of tea. More people arrived, including RSPB ecologist Jane Sears and a contingent from the South Downs National Park.

We gathered outside, mugs in hand, and stood in a circle while Jane explained the history of the field cricket and why further translocations were necessary. Then we departed in a convoy of cars to the southern part of the reserve at Tankersford, where the species was thriving. Mike briefed the team:

"Field crickets have almost identical habitat requirements to woodlarks. We need to be careful not to disturb woodlarks who are settling down to nest." In his most recent recce, Mike had found the larks on adjacent compartments but not at the donor site; nevertheless, if we saw signs of nesting activity we were to back away and look for crickets elsewhere.

"We have two people with us who are licenced to catch and handle field crickets, and their licenses cover the rest of us for this collecting session. So please do not teach anyone else how to catch crickets and do not do it without a licence-holder present or if it is not part of an approved conservation programme."

He pointed to a line of birch trees about 400 yards away. "That's where we reintroduced them originally, and they have spread all through here." He gestured with his arm to indicate the scale of the insects' expansion across about 20 acres. Jane showed us the best vegetation to collect for what she called 'tickling sticks' – soft rush, stiff enough to be capable of being pushed down the burrows, soft enough to pose no threat to the crickets. We each collected a few spears of rush.

"You'll need to be patient", said Jane. "With this cold weather, they won't be very responsive." We were there to capture six to eight male and six to eight female crickets between us, the number specified on the license, using a technique described 240 years earlier by Gilbert White:

> Where violent methods will not avail, more gentle means will often succeed; and so it proved in the present case; for, though a spade be too boisterous and rough an implement, a pliant stalk of grass, gently insinuated into the caverns, will probe their windings to the bottom, and quickly bring out the inhabitant; and thus the humane inquirer may gratify his curiosity without injuring the object of it. It is remarkable that, though these insects are furnished with long legs behind, and brawny thighs for leaping, like grasshoppers; yet when driven from their holes they show no activity, but crawl along in a shiftless manner, so as easily to be taken: and again, though provided with a curious apparatus of wings, yet they never exert them when there seems to be the greatest occasion.

Mike found a cricket burrow and pointed out its diagnostic features, including a 'patio' of bare ground, and compared it with a nearby minotaur beetle burrow, with its characteristic ring of discarded spoil. Then he demonstrated the tickling technique. We spread out among the heather and the gorse and began searching. Occasionally a voice would call out to Mike – "is this a cricket burrow? What about this one?" Then the calling died down, before resuming again: "got one! Lost it! Quick, grab a bag!"

After half an hour someone called "what are we up to?" and Mike called back "I've got three females and one male."

I was having no luck, and stood to straighten my back and survey the scene. The heath was not as a White or a Hardy would have recognised. It was scarred from a ravaging that had taken place 15 years earlier, scars that will one day heal completely, but now betrayed this as a working conservation landscape.

Hundreds of stumps of pine and strews of brash pocked the landscape, creating a temporary visual jar and a permanent ecological improvement. In that moment twenty-two raised bottoms in assorted shades of denim, canvas and moleskin also adorned the scene, a picture of sheer collective concentration of will and effort. I immediately thought of Vermeer's *The Lacemaker*, the genius of which, as Salvador Dalí pointed out, lay in the fact that the whole painting, and the subject's whole being, is focused in on a needle that is, in fact, hidden from view. I imagined Gilbert enlisting helpers to lay on the grass of the Short Lythe: presumably they would have adopted less indecorous poses, but the same expressions of concentration at the other end. I reflected that almost everything we know about the œconomy – to use Gilbert's word – of *Gryllus campestris,* he taught us.

At first we attempted to dig them out with a spade, but without any great success; for either we could not get to the bottom of the hole, which often terminated under a great stone; or else, in breaking up the ground, we inadvertently squeezed the poor insect to death. Out of one so bruised we took a multitude of eggs, which were long and narrow, of a yellow colour, and covered with a very tough skin. By this accident we learned to distinguish the male from the female; the former of which is shining black, with a golden stripe across his shoulders; the latter is more dusky, more capacious about the abdomen, and carries a long sword-shaped weapon at her tail, which probably is the instrument with which she deposits her eggs in crannies and safe receptacles.

The males only make that shrilling noise perhaps out of rivalry and emulation, as is the case with many animals which exert some sprightly note during their breeding time: it is raised by a brisk friction

of one wing against the other. They are solitary
beings, living singly male or female, each as it may
happen: but there must be a time when the sexes
have some intercourse, and then the wings may be
useful perhaps during the hours of night. When the
males meet they will fight fiercely, as I found by some
which I put into the crevices of a dry stone wall,
where I should have been glad to have made them
settle. For though they seemed distressed by being
taken out of their knowledge, yet the first that got
possession of the chinks would seize upon any that
were obtruded upon them with a vast row of serrated
fangs. With their strong jaws, toothed like the shears
of a lobster's claws, they perforate and round their
curious regular cells, having no fore-claws to dig, like
the mole-cricket. When taken in hand I could not but
wonder that they never offered to defend themselves,
though armed with such formidable weapons. Of such
herbs as grow before the mouths of their burrows
they eat indiscriminately; and on a little platform,
which they make just by, they drop their dung; and
never, in the day-time, seem to stir more than two
or three inches from home. Sitting in the entrance of
their caverns they chirp all night as well as day from
the middle of the month of May to the middle of July;
and in hot weather, when they are most vigorous,
they make the hills echo; and, in the stiller hours of
darkness, may be heard to a considerable distance.

The one significant error in White's letter to Barrington was
his assumption that crickets must at some point take to the air.

Not many summers ago I endeavoured to transplant
a colony to the terrace in my garden, by boring deep
holes in the sloping turf. The new inhabitants stayed
some time, and fed and sung; but wandered away by

degrees, and were heard at a farther distance every morning; so that it appears that on this emergency they made use of their wings in attempting to return to the spot from which they were taken.

It was fundamentally because of their flightlessness that we were there that April day. At Selborne, if they had disappeared from the Short Lythe in about 1790, four years before Gilbert White's death, it is possible they recolonised sometime later, having only cart-tracks and the traffic levels of the late eighteenth century to contend with. 21st century Farnham Heath is divided in two by The Reeds Road. The earlier reintroduction had seen them spread from the far edge of the southern half of the heath north-eastwards onto more recently restored areas, and it was clear that they were capable of walking 200–300 yards in a season – in a lifetime, in other words. If we were able to collect the six males and six females we had come for, they were destined to be released to colonise the northern portion of the reserve, which they would be unlikely to reach unaided from the wrong wide of the road.

My colleague Emma Burt, who was taken on by Back from the Brink to oversee social media communications and to support the projects' community engagement work, found a burrow and managed to coax a cricket out, only for it to scuttle back. I was standing nearby, and when she managed to coax it a second time, I covered the burrow with my finger and Emma caught it – a male. The sun had been slowly melting through the mist and as the temperature rose, the crickets became more responsive. In the distance, a woodlark sang, a sweet, rippling scale in descending semitones.

With us was another Mike – Edwards – who is one of a handful of people licensed to supervise the collection of field crickets. He carried out the original assessment of Farnham as a potential translocation site in June 2002 and decided it would be perfect even though it was still covered in trees at that time. Mike C was taken on the following September and made it his mission to remove the trees, bring back grazing and help rescue the field cricket from oblivion. I had not yet found a cricket of my own, but as the air and the soil warmed, a jewel of a beetle accelerated from a standing start a few feet away: iridescent, metallic green, powered by chrome-red legs and sand-heat, the green tiger beetle is the agile predator of the micro-deserts of bare ground between the tussocks. Mike E explained to me exactly why sandy heath is perfect for crickets.

"As the sun comes up they come to the edge of the burrow to warm up, in fact they heat up almost to death. Then they go back in to cool down. It seems to be essential for the moulting process, as each instar outgrows its outer casing. It needs to shed one skin and harden off the next a.s.a.p. Also they can't metabolise food at below 10°C. Sandy soils are brilliant because they heat up and cool down quickly".

Suddenly, the calling resumed.

"I've got a male!"

"Bag coming!"

"How many's that?

"Female here!" etc.

Mike declared the hunt over when his assistant Leah Bell-Jones held up thirteen clear polythene bags, each containing a handful of grass and a dark-brown thimble-sized insect – seven males and six females. It was a five-minute drive to the release site, and Leah and I sat in the back of Mike's car, where I was able to get a close look at the crickets through the bags. Gilbert White's succinct description can hardly be improved upon. As I examined them, I could easily imagine them forging their brief lives underground, their tough-looking carapaces and bullet shape making light work of excavating the sandy soil. They were still nymphs: tenth instars; in other words they had grown and shed nine earlier coats of tough chitin and now occupied their tenth exoskeleton. They were already looking like small versions of the fully mature adults they would be in another six weeks' time. As we reassembled at their new destination on the heath to the east of the RSPB office, the weather warmed considerably. We released them a pair at a time, every 15 to 20 yards, and watched as they scuttled into the wavy hair-grass and the creeping cinquefoil. A tree pipit parachuted over the site, as if offering a blessing in song.

I had come a long way to help in the translocation of a baker's dozen field crickets. I provided no expertise, just another pair of hands, and in any case failed to find a cricket of my own. I can probably claim to have helped Emma secure hers by blocking its retreat back into its burrow, but in truth I was there for another reason altogether: for creative inspiration.

Sounds do not always give us pleasure according to their sweetness and melody; nor do harsh sounds always displease. We are more apt to be captivated or disgusted with the associations which they promote, than with the notes themselves. Thus the shrilling of the field-cricket, though sharp and stridulous, yet marvellously delights some hearers, filling their minds with a train of summer ideas of everything that is rural, verdurous, and joyous.[9]

Two months after the translocation I returned to the Heath. With me were two friends whose business is sound, Peter Sheppard Skærved and Mihailo Trandafilovski, both violinists and composers. For two years Peter and I had talked about working together, ever since our mutual friend the composer Edward Cowie introduced us as likely kindred spirits. I had temporarily stopped composing as my writing commitments increased, but found time to work with other musicians and composers, or at least plan future projects together. My day job was by then part-time, as part of the Back from the Brink team, a perfect final role before retiring from the RSPB. It gave me a renewed focus on threatened species, and I was keen to complement my official responsibilities with a private project of my own. For several years I have sought out artists who are inspired by the natural world, especially those who, like me, are keen to explore how the arts can make a direct and specific difference for nature. Each time Peter and I met, and the more we spoke, we knew there was something we wanted to do but for a while its exact nature was elusive. We needed a nucleus around which our vague ideas could crystallise. When Jane Sears and Mike Coates presented their field cricket proposals for inclusion in the Back from the Brink programme, I found myself drawn to an insect to which I had never before paid much attention. I had read about it in *The Natural History of Selborne* and knew that it was the dedicatee of at least one John Clare poem. I had listened to its stridulating in Spain and France and realised how much the sound-world that White and Clare had inhabited had changed. As an invertebrate, it belonged to a vast, mostly unloved, invariably undervalued, and unmeasurably important Division of the animal kingdom. I have long and often wondered how conservationists could help engender a wider appreciation of the fragility of life as long as the ecological underpinning that invertebrates bestow is so depreciated. Sometimes, it seems, the rigorous arguments set out by evidence-led environmentalists are persuasive to some people but leave others unmoved. Perhaps if artists and conservationists joined forces we could find a way to help appreciate more fully the workings and beauty of the Lilliputians and their world.

Peter and I agreed that we would devote a day – it became an afternoon and an evening – to exploring the world of the field cricket, its heathland landscape, its sonic environment, its place in ecology and imagination. We would explore together with anyone who cared to join us, and about 30 people did.

We started with an afternoon walk over the heath. It was hot, and before we set off across open country, Mike C gathered us together in the shade of some of the remaining pine trees and summarised the management history of Farnham Heath. There was a long period of stability between the Bronze Age and the enclosures of the nineteenth century, during which the management cycles, common rights and customs of the heath were gradually established. Then the better land was converted into tenanted or owner-occupied farmland from which the commoners were excluded, leaving the remaining heath fragmented, and progressively abandoned. From the 1950s, the Forestry Commission and private forestry companies pursued vigorous commercial afforestation programmes over most of the unenclosed land and any enclosed plots that had proved too poor to sustain agriculture. Across the heath – even then still often referred to by Thomas Hardy's term 'the waste' – any location could be a first resort of developers seeking to build roads or housing. Towards the end of the twentieth century, in a bid to rescue the little that remained, conservation organisations acquired what they could. Then in 2002, the RSPB took the bold step of acquiring even the afforested land, now covered in mature trees, recognising that heathland could be restored and the fragments reconnected by a policy of felling and removing trees, with some of the necessary investment covered by the sale of the timber.

"It's basically the standard historical pattern of heathland everywhere in southern England", said Mike. "The differences are just a matter of what proportions got enclosed, built upon and planted up and how much is being restored."

Within four years of enclosure, in 1857 Charles Darwin walked this heath and noticed an immediate effect on the landscape. Scots pine had started spreading of its own accord: long before the vast 20th century plantations, smaller clumps of what Darwin called Scotch fir had been planted on neighbouring high ground but had never spread into the heath itself. In 1853 thirteen lots totalling 286 acres were fenced off, excluding commoners' cattle that had roamed across the unenclosed heath. Within the enclosed plots young pines were sprouting in considerable density. Darwin examined the unenclosed heath closely, scrutinising the ground between the heather:

I found a multitude of seedlings and little trees, which
had been perpetually browsed down by the cattle.
In one square yard, at one point some hundreds of
yards distant from one of the old clumps, I counted
thirty-two little trees; and one of them, judging from
the rings of growth, had during twenty-six years tried
to raise its head above the stems of the heath, and
had failed. No wonder that, as soon as the land was
enclosed, it became thickly clothed with vigorously
growing young firs. Yet the heath was so extremely
barren and so extensive that no one would ever
have imagined that cattle would have so closely and
effectually searched it for food.[10]

Realising that grazing by large herbivores was one of many factors that limited the distribution of plants, eliminating some but with others able to withstand relatively high pressure,

Darwin summarised his Farnham observations in the third chapter of *On the Origin of Species*, alongside many other examples of what he called *The Struggle for Survival.*

Each time a resinous gust reached us from the nearby pines, Peter and Mihailo exchanged glances: the smell, Peter explained, resides permanently in every violinist's nostrils, from the dust of the rosin that stictions the bow. As we walked the acres, it was repeatedly the small things that were eminent, once we had mentally recalibrated to their scale. A knot of people gathered spontaneously to examine a clump of common cudweed, a low, unpretty flower of harsh terrain. One participant noted how sheep's sorrel, whose red female flower-spikes add the odd highlight to the dun heath landscape, when collected in a low depression of recently-disturbed ground, appeared at a certain distance like a pool of blood. The five-foot high remnant of a silver birch, killed by a past gale and now proudly and sedately decaying, attracted everyone's attention, which, when zoomed in, settled upon a male rhinoceros beetle.[11] It is a perfectly-proportioned polished-mahogany miniature of its mammalian name-sake, less than an inch long, but rugged and built for combat.

Words were being jotted into small, cheap notebooks that I had handed out, hoping that later in the evening, some might be shared. I was hoping for a collective record of the day, recalling something the painter Lucian Freud once said: "A picture should be the reconstruction of an event not the illustration of an object". I had something of the same sentiment in mind: a word-picture that could only have come from that place, at that time.

There is something in the music of birds and insects that they perceive in a High Definition that their artless instruments produce but which our crude receivers are not tuned to hear. I have often wondered, what can the cricket hear that we cannot hear? Peter had been exploring the same question and revealed fine, hidden detail in the cricket's song by slowing recordings down a few times. Then he slowed the calls further, to beyond even the insect's capabilities of discernment, 500 times slower. He likened the results to a multiply-layered polyphony that recalled Tallis's *Spem in Allium*. Peter transcribed the sounds onto paper and made *Six Calls* for two violins, which he and Mihailo played that evening in an old translocated waggon-shed at the Rural Life Centre.

Mihailo had brought two of his own compositions, inspired by the sounds and movements of insects and their high-octane lives, as companion pieces for Telemann's Lilliputian Suite. The duo added pieces by two 20th century composers whose works explore the fine grain of natural sound: Bartók and Scelsi. Between each piece of music, Peter invited participants on the earlier walk to share the words they had found on the heath. The dead birch stump seemed to have been a particular and unexpected focal point:

The stark bare wood of an old stump breaks through the greenery in act of defiance. The line came from a substantial essay written on the spot and captured the paradox of a dead tree asserting itself. Four words from a poem made the paradox plain: *dead but still alive*. The explanations were succinct: *bleached bones* as a habitat for *charismatic microfauna, one of the invertebrate Big Five*: two authors finding a resonance between rhinoceroses minor and major.[12]

Speaking off the cuff, Mike offered a heartfelt recollection: "When we first did the tree-clearing work it was controversial, the local papers were full of angry letters denouncing what we were doing. But I went out into the very first clearing that we made on a crisp winter's day, late February 2005; the ash from the bonfires where we burnt the brash was still warm, there was still timber stacked by the side of the road waiting to go. Beautiful blue sky, and in that sky was a dot. And that dot was pouring forth the most wonderful song, mellow, fluty, slightly melancholy, but so much an affirmation of life. That was the first woodlark. The first woodlark to have sung from that spot for fifty or sixty years."

Dusk fell. The music and readings were over, and into a fine, lemon-and-lilac sunset we walked out of the waggon shed to listen to an evensong of insect sound that suffused the heath. It was a song of success: as we turned onto a track at the edge of the RSPB reserve, we noticed the chorus was surrounding us. Over the course of two summers, crickets had spread onto neighbouring grassland and paddocks. This much Mike knew already, and he was working with the next-door farmer, who was pleased to cooperate. But there was a second new site, unknown until this evening. It was a confirmation of the one detail missing from Gilbert White's account: their ability to cover considerable distance on foot at speed.

A gentle, rattling chatter ran through the group as we walked into the diminishing light. It was the high season for cricket song, a collective stridulating that now impregnated the evening air again, after decades of silence. The group fell quiet when a second sound interfused with the first: the churring of a nightjar. Both songs shared the same sonic property of being impossible to pin down as to their source (recalling Mark Twain: '…the tiresome chirping of a cricket that no human ingenuity could locate…').[13] It was to hear singing the very heath: *resonant arbusta* in two different registers. I sensed that there was encrypted gossip all around.

SEVEN

Narrow-headed ant

The biologists B.K. Hölldobler and E.O. Wilson said:[1] "Let us not despise the lowly ants, but honour them. For a while longer at least, they will help to hold the world in balance to our liking, and they will serve as a reminder of what a wonderful place it was when we first arrived."

If conservation means to restore a mutually-rewarding relationship between the human and the non-human world, and if this begins with not despising but honouring, then invertebrates present us with a challenge. Few are loved, many are loathed or feared, and all the others – some 40,000 species in the UK[2] and perhaps 10 million worldwide[3] – are simply disregarded. Gilbert White understood that the animals we despise (in the literal and ambiguous sense of 'look down upon') are connected to humans in vital ways. In 1777 he wrote:

> The most insignificant insects and reptiles[4] are of
> much more consequence, and have much more
> influence on the economy of nature, than the

incurious are aware of; and are mighty in their effect, from their minuteness which renders them less an object of attention; and from their numbers and fecundity. Earth-worms, though in appearance a small and despicable link in the chain of nature, yet, if lost would make a lamentable chasm.

It is impossible to overstate the revolutionary nature of this view, at a time when even farmers believed that earthworms were pests. He goes on to suggest that 'a good monography of worms would afford much entertainment and information at the same time, and open a large and new field of natural history.' 104 years later Charles Darwin obliged, when he wrote up a lifetime's research on the earthworm in his last book, *The Formation of Vegetable Mould Through the Action of Worms, With Observations on Their Habits.* For many years it sold more copies than *On the Origin of Species*. Its final paragraph includes these words:

The plough is one of the most ancient and most valuable of man's inventions; but long before he existed the land was in fact regularly ploughed, and still continues to be thus ploughed, by earth-worms. It may be doubted whether there are many other animals which have played so important a part in the history of the world, as have these lowly organised creatures.

White and Darwin built their understanding of ecology by imagining the unimaginable, a world without insects and worms. Such a world could be contemplated only in their thought-experiments. One of their direct intellectual descendants was American marine biologist Rachel Carson, who in the 1950s had no need to resort to imagination. For two decades, the combined ingenuity of chemists, entomologists, marketeers and manufacturers had been devoted to waging war on insects, based on the monumentally ignorant view that killing them indiscriminately guaranteed killing the species they regarded as pests.

In the 1930s a South American ant, *Solenopsis invicta*, arrived in the United States. By 1957 it had spread across much of the south east and was causing widespread alarm. I have direct experience of an encounter with the insect which came to be given the distinctly American English name of 'red imported fire ant' or RIFA. Once, in Texas, I stood on a mound of earth, watching some now-forgotten bird. I soon had the distinct sensation that I was standing in a flame, indeed for a second or two that is exactly what I thought, and I looked down and stepped hurriedly away. At the same moment a passer-by called out "you're standing in a fire ant's nest!". It was a sharp, painful sensation but not one that I would have attributed straight away to an insect. The pain soon subsided, but their sting is known to cause fatal allergic reactions in rare cases.

Rachel Carson was already a successful nature writer and a respected research biologist when in 1957 the United States Department of Agriculture began a fire ant eradication programme. Their principal weapon was DDT[5] and other pesticides sprayed from aeroplanes flown over vast tracts of land, paying little regard to the people and communities below, and none to the wildlife. In January 1958 Carson's friend, Olga Owens Huckins, witnessed the agonies of birds following aerial spraying against mosquitoes near her home and wrote to *The Boston Herald*, describing the experience in harrowing detail. She forwarded a copy of her letter to Carson, who promptly became a dedicated researcher-campaigner, uncovering more and more cases of ecological and human health damage. She realised that many of the new miracle chemicals were persistent in the environment and accumulated in birds' bodies, so that small doses quickly built up to lethal levels. As she compiled more and more evidence for her next book, the title she had originally chosen for a single chapter on birds was elevated to the front cover and *Silent Spring* became one of the foundation stones of a modern, ecologically-literate environmental movement.

At 1.11pm on 26 November 2018 the endangered narrow-headed ant *Formica exsecta* returned to Bovey Heathfield nature reserve after an absence of fourteen years. Stephen Carroll marked the time precisely, so personal was its significance: he had for years been one of a very few people to concern themselves with the fate of this little-known species. Until 1846 the narrow-headed ant was unregarded, warranting not even the faint distinction of a name and identity of its own. First described scientifically by Finnish entomologist Wilhem Nylander, it was located near Bournemouth in 1865, and over the following thirty-seven years Britain's small community of myrmecologists found it in the New Forest, the Isle of Wight, and, in 1902, the extensive heathlands around Bovey Tracey in Devon. Apart from a small and genetically distinct Scottish population discovered in Speyside in 1909, no population has been found in the UK away from the heaths of the West Country and Hampshire. Even as the species became better known and entomologists were adding new sites to its known range, its decline had begun and it was already being lost from some areas. Towns were expanding, and the unloved heathland surrounding them was the obvious place onto which they could spread. By 1910, 45 years after the ants were first discovered there, the Bournemouth colonies had vanished. The Isle of Wight lost its population three years later, both places having been built upon. By 1993 the narrow-headed ant was found in four remaining sites; ten years later one of them, Bovey Heathfield, was earmarked for development. The heath had already been encroached upon on all sides by industrial estates and housing and had shrunk to a 35-acre patch. Six

nests were lost as the neglected heath scrubbed over, leaving a single vulnerable colony. Stephen Carroll was among the campaigners who opposed the development plans and fought to save the remaining remnant of heathland.

"As well as the ant, there were still populations of heath potter wasp, grasshopper hunter wasp, characteristic heathland specialists," Stephen told me as we surveyed the remaining fragment from a low, rounded hillock at its centre. "Developers and planners thought of it as a place where people got up to no good and saw it as wasteland. Actually, it was probably always a place where people came for walks with the dog or a bit of birdwatching."

The campaigners persuaded the local council to shelve plans for the final destruction of Bovey Heathfield and the land passed into the hands of the Devon Wildlife Trust. It was too late for the narrow-headed ant, though. The final colony disappeared in 2004, leaving a single remaining English population at nearby Chudleigh Knighton heath.

"Every year some piece of heathland in the country gets damaged or destroyed by fire. Imagine if a fire ripped through Chudleigh," said Stephen. "We have to make Chudleigh as good as it can be, and start experimenting with moving nests back into former areas. The problem is, we know very little about this species, so we're now studying its ecology, population structure, even taking a few nests into captivity, to learn what we can before it's too late."

It was September 2019, and I was visiting the project for the second time. My first visit was the previous October, a few weeks before the historic moment when Stephen supervised the removal of five nests from Chudleigh Knighton to Bovey.[6]

Chudleigh Knighton Heath is a Devon Wildlife Trust reserve and is a fragment of the landscape that once stretched for miles across an area known locally as the Bovey Basin. From the reserve entrance I could hear the chugging of an engine of some kind coming from a compound 200 yards away. Stephen explained that although the Trust manages the reserve, the land is owned by a minerals company that had started to drill test pits. When the local clay extraction company WBB Minerals was bought out, the land passed into the ownership of the multinational Sibelco.

"No-one knows what the test pits are supposed to test," he said, "but if they are investigating whether to mine the whole site's clay reserves, then the narrow-headed ant will go extinct in England."[7]

There was a group of us on the day of that first visit, including three of my colleagues from the Back from the Brink national team, and the local project team of Stephen and three volunteer colleagues. Between us, we were to survey the site for ant nests, to update the site records. I went off to the right with John Walters, a freelance entomologist and wildlife painter, whose face I recognised. He is often on television as a regular contributor to *Springwatch*, an all-round naturalist and invertebrate enthusiast. We threaded ourselves between tussocks of purple moor grass or *Molinia*, as fieldworkers prefer to call it, brushed by purple-pink carillons of bell heather, through low gorse bushes spiny enough to prickle our shins through our trousers. We moved through a mainly open landscape dotted with small multi-trunked oak trees, old coppice that would once have been part of the economy of the common, when this was a working landscape. We moved among a band of quiet, docile North Devon bullocks in assorted colours including glossy black, dappled white and the traditional Red Ruby, part of a herd established by the Devon Wildlife Trust to maintain the habitat in the traditional way.

We were looking for low mounds made up of vegetable material – short lengths of grass, pine needles and the like – built into a tussock of *Molinia*. Some were easier to find than others, marked by lengths of blue wool tied to nearby grass stems, having been located and marked in earlier searches. These previously logged mounds each had an inch-square tile of roofing felt on top: John had discovered that the ants congregate under the tile for warmth, bringing their pupae with them. This meant that John could check under the tile, raising it for no more than a second, to check the presence of ants. The insects' response was instant and aggressive. John instinctively flicked his wrist at the first bite, sending the ants back onto their nest, except one that continued to run around on his hand. I was keen to get a closer look and tried ineffectually to tempt the insect onto my finger. John caught it deftly between the finger and thumb of his left hand, holding it with exactly the right amount of pressure to keep it fast but unharmed. A folding magnifying lens appeared in his right hand with the suddenness of a concealed switchblade and he handed it to me. I saw that the ant's abdomen was dark brown, the rest of its body reddish, somewhat darker so on its head.

"Can you see that the back of its head is concave? It's the main distinguishing feature."

We came across three nests ten feet apart in an equilateral triangle. John knew them, had marked them with blue wool, and had assigned each a GPS location that enabled them, and all the nests found to date, to be mapped precisely and any changes to be easily noted. Each was domed, around ten inches in diameter and a foot tall, but built asymmetrically, with more of their surface facing south for warmth. They were all covered by what John described as a 'thatched roof' made from grass, heather and other dry plant fragments, providing highly effective insulation.

"There was a fourth nest – just... *here* – but now it's deserted, so they've moved. Some of them may have joined *this* nest," he said, squatting beside the nest closest to the former site.

Across the central part of the heath we found nests every few yards, but the map revealed that they were arranged in obvious clusters. As we reached each cluster, John squatted into the tall heath vegetation, recording the presence or absence of ants, and the presence or absence of the white pupae, like small grains of rice and referred to as 'brood', under the felt tiles.

"I wasn't expecting them to have brood this late" he said. "The presence of brood means there are one or more queens in the nest; we don't know yet if the converse is true."

Next we monitored two nests about four feet apart. "Both used to have *exsecta* colonies, then one was abandoned and *fusca* [black wood ant *Formica fusca*] moved in, now they've abandoned it too," John explained, before crouching at another nest.

"*Lasius niger*," he said. "The common black garden ant – you see the very fine soil it's made of, just like in your garden." We continued our round, as if making house-calls, updating records for the week. John explained each nest's case history in brief:

"The week before last that nest was abandoned, and last week they appeared at this new nest two and a half metres away. They must have carried the entire brood with them and a lot of the nest material. Why they do that, no-one knows. Maybe that birch is casting too much shade now that the days are shortening. Perhaps they've moved here to prepare for spring."

"It sounds like moving house is not exceptional," I replied, and John reeled off a short litany of explained and unexplained facts and phenomena:

...nest material comprises short lengths of grass, grass seeds, caterpillar and snail droppings...

...some nests contain both *fusca* and *exsecta*; then the following week one or other of them may have gone...

...narrow-headed ants are easier to find because they are aggressive. *Fusca* just run away into the undergrowth...

...the ants' foraging range was believed to be a five-metre radius from the nest but this project is questioning that: Betsy Vulliamy, a volunteer on the project, has been marking them individually and found them farther afield, and up to two metres up trees, probably after aphids...

I squatted to watch the ants at closer quarters, half-listening to John. Soon I was imagining myself a visitor in their Mildendo. Their hyper-crowded, three-dimensional cities are something out of *Blade Runner,* chiaroscuro worlds that never sleep, whose architecture and its inhabitants are one and the same, where vast armies are genetically programmed to perform endless menial tasks for the common good. Command and control are everything, yet they emanate from an intangible nerve centre distributed throughout the commonwealth. There will be ants climbing to the uppermost reaches of the nest to absorb solar energy at its under-surface and returning to transfer the heat of their own bodies through the labyrinth, a living hypocaust. Others ferry their sibling pupae through the writhing tangle of vegetation, detritus and co-workers, forever up and down between storeys, constantly monitoring and regulating temperature in the brood.

Field workers had already left the city for forage. A brief, narrow, slanting shaft of sunlight pierced the overcast of cloud that had kept the heath's colours muted all day. I imagined those few seconds of increased warmth and enriched light and their effect on the microworld beneath. Each few photons energise in a birch leaf the synthesis of vital sugars. It is an industrial complex: from point of manufacture, the sugar is transported under pressure in pipelines built into the tree's structure. Aphids tap the supply-lines and siphon off a percentage. The ants tend the aphids, taking their own cut in the form of honeydew. In return they protect the aphids from ladybirds and other predators. It is a time-proven system that relies on a perpetual stalemate between trust and menace; yet the aphids are a more ancient life-form than the ants, by some 140 million years. They did not co-evolve as mutualists, rather, at some point a deal was struck at genome level, in all likelihood a truce between onetime predator and prey. Replete, the ants return to their nests.

Inside, at the heart of the citadel, resides the queen, the oldest and most venerated member of ant society. Most colonies will be organised around her needs alone, thousands of loyal subjects programmed to protect, feed and pamper her, their roles and responsibilities passed down through short-lived generations while she lives on for decades. One narrow-headed ant queen was known to have lived for 27 years, I could hear John saying. Other colonies differ: in so-called polygyne colonies several queens may reign simultaneously. For a polygynous colony to thrive, it must rearrange its sex ratio to produce a larger proportion of male offspring, adjust its social structure, reform its hierarchy system. The choice between these two alternative cultures is under the collective control of the commonwealth, according to arcane rules that have never been revealed to outsiders like John and Stephen. The queens are the breeding stock; they mate and lay eggs, electively fertilising some that grow into diploid females – daughters of two parents and containing chromosomes from both – and depositing some eggs unfertilised, to grow into haploid males, containing only the queen's DNA.

A few weeks earlier, the warm air rising above the heath would have glistened with sunlight reflected by tens of thousands of insect wings. In the morning, at the top of each colony mound, male ants emerged. For several hours they had been undergoing a metamorphosis, emerging in their short-lived winged form at the start of their last few hours of life. Yearling queens, virgins all, were close behind, also awaiting their first and only flight. On another visit, Stephen would explain:

"Nuptial flights always seem to happen within a few days either side of July 21, early in the morning. You see males and queens gathering on top of nests and climbing up grass stems to catch a breeze. Not a swarm as such, more a queue."

The males are programmed to do nothing for the few months of their lives but to live in the constant warmth and dark of the colony receiving food direct from the mouths of their sisters in preparation for this day; and then to shimmer into the air in the hope of catching a mate, bringing her to the ground, mating and dying. Greatly outnumbering the queens, the overwhelming majority would fail and die anyway, unable to feed themselves or even to recognise food, if unaccompanied by the scent of their sisters' pheromones.

The old queens will remain in the colony, still with years of egg-laying before them, their one day of flight and sex receding ever farther into the past, their reserves of stored sperm unspent yet. The newly-emerged queens move out for good but cannot found colonies on their own. Once mated, narrow-headed ant queens must seek out a queenless nest, or more often the nest of a different species entirely.

"Usually *fusca* and possibly *rufa* [southern wood ant *Formica rufa*]," said Stephen. "They eventually oust the host queen and have the host workers help them raise their own brood. Eventually, the colony consists of only the invading queen's offspring. The precise mechanism has possibly never been seen or described. From what we know of the southern wood ant which also brood-parasitises *Formica fusca*, the invading queen enters a host nest and discreetly loiters there for a time acquiring the nest smell and/or other chemical cues. At some point presumably the *exsecta* queen must attack and kill the host queen. Timing must be critical – when the *fusca* nest has enough workers to carry out brood rearing duties, but not so well established and numerous that they would find and exterminate the invading queen."

At the southern corner of the heath, close to the A38 road, I spotted a young man with some strange-looking equipment. He introduced himself as Ziad Ibbini, a PhD student at the University of Plymouth. He appeared to be photographing the sky using what he described as a 360° hemispheric fish-eye camera. It was perched a foot or so above the ground on a short, jointed tripod which itself looked like the arching limbs of a huge, alien, three-legged, one-eyed, sky-gazing invertebrate. The camera stood astride a narrow-headed ants' nest and I noticed some short, flat wooden sticks protruding from the ground.

"I've put iButton temperature probes on the ends of those lolly sticks. I'm collecting a lot of data that needs processing before I can make complete sense of it but already we've found that the daytime temperature in the nest varies between 30–40 °C, while it's only 10–25° in the soil." A few days later, having downloaded the data into his computer, he emailed me his latest findings:

> The mean pH at the nest was higher than the soil pH 1m away. Possibly due to the dead vegetation decomposing and releasing alkalizing compounds into the soil, or it could have already been more alkaline, and the ants are instead selecting these areas to build their nest upon.
>
> The Leaf Area Index calculated from the hemispherical photos was higher the further from the zenith (the very centre of the hemispherical photograph or the top of the fish-eye lens from

a camera point of view). This suggests that the ants situate the nests where most of the vegetation is located near the horizon. Therefore keeping the points in the sky where the sun is at its brightest free from vegetation.

The total and average sunfleck frequency (gaps between leaves where sunlight is able to penetrate and reach the ground) was very low for the majority of the nests. A characteristic result of very open areas, as there is less opportunity for sunflecks to occur due to the minimal canopy cover.

Another email arrived a few days later:

I have just processed the data from the second batch of loggers I put in (involving placing 8 loggers in inactive and active nest structures for 16 days). It appears from a couple of summary graphs that I have created so far that it may indeed be the nest structure itself causing the vastly different temperature patterns found in the nests. The trendlines for the 8 temperature plots closely followed the same pattern and there wasn't substantial variation between them. However, it is hard to say now if this is the case until I do some comprehensive data analysis.

On the Heath with Stephen the following year we were looking for new nests. He had clearly got his eye in, while I found it difficult to tell a moor-grass tussock with thatch from a tussock with natural debris. He knelt next to a nest, took a length of turquoise wool from his bag and tied it round a sapling.

"Often when we find a nest it's close to a small birch sapling, we think because that means there's a ready supply of aphids. When there are no aphids, they feed on buds and vetch, getting nectar and honeydew, so floral diversity within the vicinity of the nest is useful. So far we haven't detected an obvious feeding strategy that governs when they turn to scavenging, preying, gleaning honeydew etc."

The new nest was a few metres from an established one, marked by a number painted in black onto a smooth grey stone that lay on the ground nearby. Nest 8 was also close to a birch sapling and Stephen pointed out a narrow-headed ant in the foliage.

"It'll be foraging brown birch aphids for honeydew. They switch between different aphid species through the season and will use shiny birch aphid when they are available."[8]

At this intricate level, researching the life of a single species and its relationship to the wider heath would be a lifetime's work. Stephen's commitment to understanding the world of this one ant did not end when he stowed his rucksack on the back of his bicycle and headed home each day.

"We assume they spend the coldest weeks of winter in the underground part of the nest. It's important to confirm what they do in winter because traditionally, that's when parts of the heath get burned as part of the management regime. A quick burn while the ants are underground won't do any harm and reduces the chances of a serious fire in the summer." As part of the team's investigations, Stephen and his colleague Betsy each took a nest home for the winter.

"We kept them in large transparent tubs. Betsy kept hers in her greenhouse, mine spent the winter in my front room. It was a more engrossing watch than Christmas TV and I learned a lot about nest housekeeping. Within eight hours, new entrances started popping up at the soil surface. After 24 hours they had created a thatched roof and repaired the interior tunnels. I fed them on fruit and any dead insects I found on the windowsill. They even set up their own midden in the corner of the tub where they put indigestible chitin from the insects I gave them, old pupa cases and stuff like that. In Betsy's they created the midden in an old honey pot. After 4 weeks workers were carrying nibbled grass stems and soil fragments to a burgeoning mound that tilted towards the light from a window."

At Bovey Heathfield the new incipient colony of translocated nests benefitted directly from Stephen's visits. From another pocket in his rucksack Stephen took a small apple and a kitchen knife. He placed wedges of apple around the nest a foot or two away in all directions and the ants immediately detected them, running over the fruit in short, one-second bursts like characters in a silent movie.

"We're giving the new arrivals a helping hand until they're established. We don't know if they'll stay put, or whether they'll move to a better spot. Ant ecology is so complex we don't yet know enough to see the heath the way they see it, we can just choose spots that appear to have the right patterns of sunlight, soil structure, grass, flowers and a proportion of saplings. There may be relationships we don't yet understand, as well as the ones we think we do, like the need for other ant species to act as hosts for the new queens. And there may be inquilines that will also benefit from what we're doing."

"Inquilines?" The Latin word *inquilinus* means 'lodger' or 'tenant' but I hadn't heard the English word before.

"An inquiline is a species that lives in the nest of another species without causing any harm. It's highly likely that there are several insects that are uniquely dependent on narrow-headed ants. There's a beetle, *Dinarda hagensi* that has not been seen in Britain for over a century and is specific to only this one species of ant. We've started looking for them."

The complexity of the interconnected lives of ants and other species, and of these to their habitat, may never be fully imagined, let alone described and understood. Over two and a half centuries of growing ecological awareness we have sought desperately to find and adapt language capable of representing the world as it is revealed to us. It is like trying to describe the unique pattern of a kaleidoscope image and then trying to explain in what way it differs from the next one. This complexity has given our planet a resilience that has seen its life systems adapt to the most extreme challenges imaginable. Life did not cease when the Chicxulub asteroid hit the Earth 66 million years ago, despite three-quarters of all plant and animal species being sent to extinction in the climate chaos that followed. While the fifth great extinction event saw nature's diversity and complexity diminish dramatically, what was to follow demonstrates that diversification has been life's inexorable goal since the beginning. If lesser extinction events are included, it is a process that has been interrupted around 26 times, although never – until now – by the actions of any one member of the global community of species.

A recent comprehensive review[9] reveals dramatic rates of decline that may lead to the extinction of 40% of the world's insect species in the coming decades. The early signs were closely tracked in the UK, where a large community of well-organised amateurs have recorded serious declines in the most easily recognised and popular species – butterflies and moths – since 1976. The plight of that other much-appreciated group, bees, was for many years a rare rallying point for the cause of insect conservation, as the obvious link to pollination and food crops translated into a human concern. More recently, media coverage has started to suggest that we are finally beginning to comprehend – and moreover care about – the fundamental importance of invertebrates to the future of life as we know it.

EIGHT

Otter

The word itself is a survivor: follow it upstream to its source. Old Norse *otr*, from Proto-Germanic **otraz*, source also of Old English *otr* or *otor*, Swedish *utter*, Danish *odder*, Dutch *otter*, Old High German *ottar*. From Proto-Indo-European **udros*, "water-creature", source also of Sanskrit *udrah*, and thence Hindi *ood*, Bengali *uda*, Tamil *oṭṭar* and Punjabi *ōṭara*. And of the Greek *hydra* "water-serpent" and *enydris* "otter"; of the Latin *lutra*, Old Church Slavonic *vydra*, Lithuanian *udra*, Old Irish *odoirne*. From some high, far-away linguistic watershed, the birthplace of countless rivulets that tumble across continents, it always carries a few droplets of the root-word **wed-* "water; wet", more ancient still.[1]

From Berwick I caught the bus to Paxton, six miles upriver and just over the border in Scotland, and at one o'clock started walking back, downstream along the left bank of the Tweed. The sky was almost cloudless, and the wide right-hand curve of the river reflected the same blue and mirrored a lone wisp of cirrus. It was mild for December. I set off to walk back to Berwick, noting flotillas of goldeneye and goosander every few hundred yards. These two ducks partition the river's resources between them, the goldeneye searching the stones for small, slow prey such as crustaceans, insect larvae and molluscs, the goosander pursuing fish in an evenly-matched contest of streamlining, fleetness and power.

There were indents of bare mud at the river edge, worn and smoothed, the kind of place where an otter might slip in and climb out, but the only footprints I could see had been imprinted by a large dog. Two miles farther downstream, four miles from the sea and with an hour to go before high tide, three grey seals were making their way upriver, and I wondered how far inland they intended going before turning back. They submerge nostrils-last, I noted. There is a long, narrow island alongside the bank that served as a high tide refuge for a few redshanks and oystercatchers, and a heron that flushed before I noticed it, uttering a loud, palindromic *Kra-a-ark!* as his slow, dark wings carried him down towards the distant estuary.

The path continued over a wooden stile which broke when I stepped on it, with a dog-bark sound that ricocheted off the water. By a congregation of crack willows harbouring flotsam from tides and spates past: yellow Holsten beer-crate, red traffic cone, two mineral lick tubs and two tree guards. Fence posts, a football, plastic bottles and driftwood. Reminders that the Tweed is both riparian and tidal here. The river was outcompeting the sea thus far, still flowing downstream, but all the while rising. I held my line at the water's edge, along a tongue of land 600 yards long, but had to double back when I realised the rising water had filled the far end of the channel that separated it from the river bank. A snipe flushed from my feet and zig-zagged back to invisibility.

Two and a half miles downstream, the path briefly deviated left along a line of sycamores twelve ranks wide that connected the left bank of the Tweed and the right bank of its tributary, the Whiteadder. Reptilian in its flow, perhaps, but this -*adder* is from *awedur*, the Old English "running water" and thence again to **wed-* the common ancestor of this river and the animal I was still seeking. I crossed the Whiteadder by a footbridge at the top of the spring tide. The Whiteadder was by now noticeably higher than the field at its right bank, where 21 blackface ewes fed under the protection of the upper foot or so of a flood defence bund. A sycamore stick floated stock still on the water, the point at which the river and the sea cancelled each other out.

Downstream, where the Whiteadder meets the Tweed, the river had overtopped and low-lying parts of the riverside fields were flooded. Holding the higher ground, I was separated from the footpath's yellow waymarker by 20 yards of water. For a fifty-yard stretch I was hemmed into the base of a hedge, able to walk along a slightly raised sheep-path by hanging by my left hand from the sheepwire at the hedge, ducking below the repeating overhang of hawthorn and dog rose, and twice twisting back a few yards having had my woollen hat snatched off my head by the thorns. Finally I was released onto an undulating bund but this led only into water, so I was forced to deviate inland through a derelict shiel, along a farm track and up into a hanger wood at a right-hand bend in the river.

The full 721 yards and 28 arches of the Royal Border railway viaduct was now in view to the right as I followed the curve of the river, before the track led uphill to the top edge of the wood, where a waymarker indicated the remaining distance to my destination – Berwick 1½ miles. The sky was still clear but the sun was now low and its light fading; the warm colours of the autumn wood offered occasional highlights within the darkening. There was enough light to enhance the winter beech leaves that covered the woodland floor and a pair of red squirrels that ran across them with a crisp rustle. Looking beyond the wood from within the gloom exaggerated the light outside, reflecting green-gold off the neighbouring ley field, and hot caramel off three roe deer that were feeding there. There were another two among the trees, betrayed by their white rumps. To the right and down through the trees beyond the lower edge of the wood, the mirrored surface of the tide-engorged river at sunset reflected a lemon-glow sky.

On the edge of town, I met three men and their Jack Russells. I asked them what they were after – rabbits? No, just letting the dogs run about. I asked the old man with the old, slow dog if he ever sees otters here.

"Nah, Ah never seen an od'er, y'd be lucky ta see an od'er."

As dusk fell, lights in the arches of the viaduct came on, changing red-green-violet-blue. I followed the path under the viaduct, and under the 'new' 1928 road crossing to the Old Bridge of 1611. Amid the deepening gloam of the walled town, the river was still reflecting the twilight, and was glass-smooth, so any otter breaking the surface would be easily seen. "Between the two bridges at low tide" was the advice I had been given.

Low tide was at 8.45 pm, and I returned to the Old Bridge an hour before, by which time the sky and the water were dark, except that the water reflected Christmas lights that adorned the lampposts at intervals along the New Bridge. The reflections, on river water now running low over its stony bed, shimmered like torches of gold and silver flame. Now there were exposed islands of flat rock riverbed and pools within them that reflected the bridge's lights. As I walked along the old bridge, the lights flashed off the dark water at irregular intervals each time I crossed a line of reflection. A heron priested the wrack-slicked river's edge (to borrow Dylan

Thomas's exactly fitting verb: ...*And in the mussel pooled and the heron / Priested shore...*),[2] barely visible in the shadow of the quay, but maybe using the Christmas lights to enhance any flash of fish in the dark water. I recalled the atmospheric opening line of *Tarka the Otter*.

> Twilight over meadow and water, the eve-star shining above the hill, and Old Nog the heron crying kra-a-ark! as his slow dark wings carried him down to the estuary.

One day in 1921 a stranger arrived at Henry Williamson's Devon cottage seeking help in rescuing an orphaned otter cub. Williamson brought it home, and his cat found contentment in the role of foster mother. One evening, however, when Williamson and the otter were enjoying a stroll together, the animal got caught in a rabbit snare and when Williamson freed him, ran off. For months he searched the countryside near his home, but never saw the otter again. *Tarka* the novel was born six years later, and with his meticulous detailing of otters' playful, curious and adventurous natures, Williamson created an instant and lasting success.

And looking over the parapet I recalled another first line – from Kathleen Raine's poem *The Marriage of Psyche:*

> He married me with a ring, a ring of bright water.

A man who had been unable to requite her love appropriated her words: *Ring of Bright Water* is Gavin Maxwell's poetic and moving memoir of life at Sandaig on the remote west coast of Scotland and of the relationships he formed with three pet otters. In combining idyll and violent tragedy, including the killing of the otter Mijbil by a road-mender with a pickaxe on a lonely Scottish lane (an event for which the rejected Raine blamed herself, having uttered a curse a few days earlier), *Ring of Bright Water* reads like a dark fairy tale. Sixty years after publication, it is perhaps best understood as the memoir of a disturbed and disturbing personality at odds with the world, seeking a kind of vicarious freedom through the animals to whom he devotes huge love but less than adequate care.

While the fascist Williamson and the closeted misanthrope Maxwell have had their personalities and reputations thoroughly reappraised, their legacy is unassailable. Their books remain among the most popular and highly-regarded English-language depictions of nature yet written, and in turn led to another reappraisal: that of our feelings for the otter itself.

Prior to otter hunting being banned in England and Wales in 1978 and in Scotland in 1982 the animal had been hunted continuously since long before Paul Haakonsson, the Viking Earl of Orkney took his men on that fateful otter hunt on the island of Rousay.[3] Mesolithic people who arrived to settle the small Inner Hebridean tidal island of Oronsay left otter remains in midden layers that document at least seven centuries of continuous year-round occupation.

Otters were valued for their fur. They were also eaten, probably mainly as a by-product of fur trapping, and are among the handful of non-piscines considered by the Catholic church to be fish, suitable therefore for eating on Fridays. In England and Wales, following a familiar pattern, utilitarian hunting merged with a growing enthusiasm for recreational hunting under the Normans and Plantagenets; and this in turn merged with the Tudor persecutions of species classed as vermin under Elizabeth I's Act of 1566. The otter's crime, of course, was to share a diet with much of the population of Britain, and especially its aristocracy. Over centuries, commoners who lived near rivers, lakes and marshes had developed an array of ingenious contraptions and skills to obtain the freshwater fish that made up a significant part of their diet, and it is unlikely that the competition would have been systematically eliminated. The fishponds built and managed for the elites, the monasteries and the great manor houses, however, were both a closely guarded resource and an irresistible temptation for poachers – human, avian and lutrine.

Henry Williamson, though not an enthusiastic hunter, joined his local otter hunt in order to gain first-hand experience of the sport he intended to write about. Otters were still plentiful in the county, despite Devon being the place where organised otter hunting with specially-bred hounds had been established longest. Otter specialist Don Jefferies suggests that the population remained high in most places until at least the middle of the eighteenth century but by 1800 the first extinctions from certain rivers were noted. Again, following a familiar pattern, the nineteenth century saw a lucrative growth in sport fishing, and with ever more skilled gamekeepers at large, pressure on otter populations increased further. But otters were never as widely or intensively hunted as foxes. At the turn of the twentieth century, when otter hunting was at its peak, there were just 23 registered hunts, a number that dropped to eleven in the years after the Second World War. By the 1950s otter numbers had fallen considerably. Otter packs saw a decline in their success rate and instituted voluntary restraints on the proportion killed among those encountered. Nevertheless, the otter was still widespread and, in many places, not uncommon. This was to change suddenly in the 1960s.

Jefferies and his colleague Paul Chanin were the first to correlate the decline of the otter with the introduction of certain new insecticides, first DDT, then particularly dieldrin and aldrin.[4] These organochlorines were the chemicals at the centre of the *Silent Spring* era of the late 1950s and 1960s, when the United States government and the agrichemical industry waged war on insects, largely irrespective of whether they were injurious, neutral or beneficial. The UK adopted the new technology in 1956, and the first bird declines were reported soon after. Dieldrin (directly applied, or as the toxic metabolite of aldrin) stayed in the environment to accumulate in the bodies of larger animals, too. As early as November 1959, reports began to circulate of a mysterious fox illness. Foxes appeared dazed, partially blind, hypersensitive to noise, and dying of thirst. Eventually, analytical techniques were developed that enabled scientists to recognise the 'illness' as poisoning by the same insecticides that were killing tens of thousands of birds. As well as affecting foxes, dieldrin was detected in 81% of otters examined between 1963 and 1973.[5,6]

The chemicals were finding their way into waterways, either carelessly sprayed into ditches and rivers, or washed off fields by the rain. Fish were killed directly and otters indirectly. Writing in 1978, Chanin and Jefferies noticed that although the use of organochlorines was restricted after 1963, and would eventually be outlawed altogether, the otter had not responded; rather, it had continued to decline. The otter's rapid disappearance over two or three decades can initially be explained by the pervasive use of lethal agrichemicals, but the latter half of the period was also a time when riparian habitat was altered dramatically. Rivers were straightened by the newly-formed Internal Drainage Boards, consortia of farmers appointed to oversee and coordinate floodplain drainage. River banks were artificially raised to protect pasture (and, increasingly, housing) from winter floods, simultaneously destroying both riverine and wet grassland habitats. Wet woodland, reedy fringes, oxbow lakes and river islands were lost, along with the otter holts and fish nurseries they harboured, and the otters they hosted.

I saw my first otter in 1979. It was a real rarity, at the nadir of the species' history, albeit in one of very few places in England where they were known to persist – Leighton Moss in Lancashire. I was an undergraduate at the University of Lancaster and a regular volunteer at Leighton, my nearest RSPB reserve. One June evening, I was sitting in the main hide looking out at a serene, still mere of open water fringed by reeds. Suddenly, a loose flock of mallards, most of whom had been drifting and slumbering on the water in the warmth of the evening, shot into the air, following the lead of the few among them who had remained alert. I searched for what had put them up, expecting a peregrine or marsh harrier somewhere in the air above them, but there was none. Then I saw the low, flat top of the otter's head and the short wake it left in the water as it crossed the mere from right to left and disappeared into the reeds.

I knew there were otters on the Tweed, because one afternoon several years ago I watched a mother and three well-grown cubs playing under the Old Bridge close to the centre of Berwick. Now I spent three unsuccessful hours on the same bridge, watching for any wake cutting through the reflected light. I had walked six miles of the river and spent several hours watching it in its brightest day colours and into its warm evening garb; three grey seals, five roe deer, two red squirrels and a fox had to serve as fare enough.

Next day, within five minutes of arriving at the river I caught a brief glimpse of a shape in the water 100 yards upstream. It reappeared closer but disappeared again immediately. Definitely an otter. It next reappeared about 50 yards away, then 30 yards, alongside the nearer pier of the first arch of the Old Bridge. It was close enough for me to see its cream-coloured canine teeth as it chewed at its catch, but each view was for a few seconds only. A dog otter. It swam round to the far side of the pier and disappeared under the second arch. I walked back downstream to get a better angle. The otter appeared on the surface, and rafted rapidly downriver for about 40 yards, before turning back, effortlessly beating into the current with a porpoise-like swimming action above and below the surface. It seemed to be working its way across the arches towards the opposite bank, exploring each wrack-covered pier in turn. My fieldnotes for 5 December 2017:

> The otter becomes the river, becomes water. It flows, it swirls, eddies, rips, rafts, drifts; it becalms, streams, gyres, abates; it swells, churns, ferments, seethes.

Loch Scridain can, like all lochs, present a gleaming, crisply outlined Kodachrome image one minute and a glowering impressionistic canvas the next. Equal proportions of mountain, sky and water are its fixed geometry; infinite gradations and angles of wind and sun determine the personality of the moment. As a sea loch, there is the state of the tide to consider as well. Exactly a year after my last visit to Mull and Iona, I was back. Jane was supposed to have come with me the first time, but had to cancel at the last minute, so we returned together. On Iona we walked north as far as the road took us; a year earlier I had overheard a woman telling a man that someone had told her that they had heard a corncrake there, in the fields by the hostel. This time we heard him; even better, we saw him: we watched his progress across the field by the wake of moving grass he made, and by following this, once or twice we caught his eye catching ours, in places where the meadow grasses grew thinner.

As we returned from the Iona ferry at Fionnphort along the Ross of Mull, where we planned to stay for a few nights, a red-bordered triangular road sign gave warning of otters for the next six miles. On the first evening we watched a female with a well-grown cub, a hundred yards east of our lodgings on the southern shore of the loch. They were feeding on the wrack that fringed the water's edge, and soon after we arrived the adult left her cub while she went to hunt a few yards offshore. She returned two minutes later with a large shore crab, dispatched at sea for processing ashore, and after eating her share returned to the open water, again returning quickly with a crab. On the female's next fishing trip, the cub joined her, farther out into the loch beyond the crabbing grounds. The mother's dives might last around twenty seconds at a time, while the cub spent more time at the surface, calling often with a short, high squeak. He made occasional short dives, at the end of which he would launch his body half out of the water, periscoping the loch for signs of his mother, calling all the while. Presently the female surfaced with a large butterfish, quickly chomped it in half, letting the tail half fall into the water; the cub practice-dived to retrieve it. The meal over, both otters porpoised to the west shore, becoming lost to view about four hundred yards away.

In the 1990s Jon Watt gained his PhD studying otters on the coast of Mull and went on to lead a field team studying sea otters in the Aleutian Islands of Alaska. On Mull he recorded the development of hunting abilities in cubs, finding that as they grew, not only did their reliance on their mother decrease and their hunting ability increase, but the proportion of crabs in their diet declined. By 13 months old, young otters were entirely self-sufficient but still continued to catch a higher proportion of crabs than experienced adults. Watt surmised that shore crabs were not a preferred prey but were relatively easy for juvenile otters to locate and capture. The apparent preference of otters for fish over crabs could be explained by their relative energetic profitability – the amount of energy gained over that expended in the search, capture and handling of each prey type. He also noted that young otters are dependent on their mothers for about three months longer on Mull than in Shetland, probably a sign of a lower abundance of prey.[7]

The next morning before five o'clock I left Jane asleep in our room and returned to the same spot, choosing two great, sea-smoothed boulders to lean against, hoping I would be mostly hidden from an otter's view. There was no wind, little cloud. Ben More towered over the opposite shore and its reflection stared back from the mirror-like near half of the loch; the distal half had a surface like frosted glass. Rippled ribbons of mist appeared in the two feet or so of air immediately above the water's surface. As I watched them dancing their slow, snaking paths to nowhere, evaporating from one place and condensing in another, I pondered what governs when and where they arise and the form they take. The surface frosting was also mysterious as to its cause: it spread to cover the whole loch as the sun appeared above the low-lying land to the east, my right, then as the sun lifted fully above the horizon, the mirror-effect returned, pushing the frosting to the west. Such ruminations filled the time as I waited, hoping the otters would return. At five-twenty, one did. It was suddenly there, about 150 yards offshore, swimming at the obsidian surface, left to right at a slow, calm pace and leaving a silver-green wake about 15 yards long. It dived, reappeared a hundred yards farther east and after a minute or so had disappeared at the eastern shore, 800 yards distant.

Between sightings I watched the shifting of the loch's colours and luminosities. It was easy, in the low-angled morning light, to tune out the landscape and to see only abstract shapes and watch their evolution. I could concentrate on imagining the otter somewhere under the skin of the loch, or out of sight among rocks. The wrack at the shore rose and fell and coiled with the breathing of the sea-loch. Its colours blended and unblended, deep, oily bronze and sun-touched copper. The same colours, belonging to the dawn slopes of Ben More and its spruces, were faithfully rendered by the brittle surface of the loch, then lost to a silent shatter at the touch of each passing breeze. The soundtrack was deceptively innocent: a descending chromatic scale from a willow warbler, hooded crow with the coarse speech of a high-tar smoker, a common sandpiper's pipe-and-trill. The rippling-water voice of a curlew, occasionally to the east, to landward, was the unseen sonic analogue of the water-otter. Herons coming and going: the *kra-a-ark!* contained a falsetto note like a boy's breaking voice. Somewhere, the otter would be eddying and gyring, live-streaming the final moments of an eelpout.

It was nearly an hour before I saw her again, 400 yards to the east and returning with the same slow, calm flow, like a small log in a deep river. I watched her for the five minutes she granted me, half of which she spent underwater in a single dive, which I timed at two minutes twenty-five seconds. Another dive seemed to last as long, until I realised that she had left, across the loch, or eastwards back to the estuary, or westwards towards the open sea. I made my way back upshore to the road, plucking a handful of aromatic bog myrtle and water mint leaves to crush and apply to my face and hands. As midge-repellent, it works well for a few minutes between applications.

Otters are difficult to survey. It was several years before even experienced researchers appreciated the scale of their disappearance, by which time they had been wiped out over the greater part of lowland England. They reached a low point at the end of the 1970s, when they had gone from everywhere except the West Country and parts of Northern England, with relatively good numbers only to be found in upland areas of Wales and Scotland. Surveying otters means surveying signs of otters – their distinctive droppings, or spraints, being the best clue. The first national otter survey took place between 1977 and 1979 and detected the presence of otters in just over 5 per cent of the 2,940 sites surveyed, all of which were known to have held them in the past.

The comeback was gradual. England's rivers were being cleaned up after nearly two centuries of industrial and urban pollution and half a century of agricultural run-off, the effects of which have recently come to light. A study[8] published in February 2020 examined long-term distribution trends in over 5000 species in 31 different taxonomic groups. A varied array of 318 freshwater species experienced a strong decline in the UK between 1970 and the mid-1990s and since then has recovered back to 1970 levels. While this is a measure of distribution (based on occupancy) and not abundance, it would suggest that freshwater wildlife has been recovering after a period of serious decline. Furthermore the upturn in the trend coincides perfectly with the implementation of the EU Urban Wastewater Treatment Directive, designed to clean up waterways and remove harmful pollutants from rivers.

As fish returned to previously sterile watercourses, and with legal protection against hunting and persecution, otters began to spread back into England from their strongholds in Devon and the Welsh border lands. Further otter surveys were carried out at regular intervals and by the time of the fourth survey, between 2000 and 2002, more than 36 per cent of the sites examined showed otter traces. Eight years later, a fifth survey saw the figure rise to nearly 60 per cent, with otters back in every English county except my own home county of Kent. They are now to be found in once-dead rivers running through cities, brought back to life through a clean-up overseen by the Environment Agency. Otters live contentedly in Stoke-on-Trent, Reading, Exeter and Leeds, as well as in many smaller towns like Thetford and Winchester.

However, while levels of the persistent organic pollutants that caused their populations to crash are now under control, new generations of chemicals are constantly being developed, with unforeseeable impacts when released into the complex natural environment outside the laboratory. Recent research suggests that the otters in England and Wales are largely healthy, but new compounds have started to appear in otter tissue samples. The same research notes an increase in reproductive abnormalities in male otters, attributed to endocrine disrupting chemicals.[9] These are compounds that cause developmental disorders and encompass many different chemical classes, including drugs, pesticides, industrial by-products and pollutants.

In south-east England an Otters and Rivers Project started in 1989 and ran for 20 years. Run by the Hampshire Wildlife Trust on behalf of all the south-eastern counties, it involved reinstating and repairing lost and damaged riparian habitat, work funded and assisted by the Environment Agency. As Hampshire otter numbers increased, their expansion into Sussex and Kent was keenly anticipated, but they remained elusive for years, with no discernible impact at all in Kent. Before 1956, otters were found in every catchment in the county. Soon they were lost, and half a century later there was no sign of the resurgence that was taking place across the rest of the country. Kent's highly fragmented landscape, with scattered remnant habitats separated by increasingly busy roads and other physical barriers is believed to be the reason Kent became the last county to see otters return.

Then, in 2011 otters were seen building holts on the banks of the Medway and the Eden. As well as the habitat improvements, otters had benefited from a sharp reduction in the volume of water extracted from rivers by water companies, farming and industry. Compared to 20 years earlier, every day around 35 million fewer litres were being taken from the River Darent, which flows along the valley where I grew up and on into the Medway. This led to a recovery in brown trout and pike, all good news for the UK's largest surviving carnivore.

Conservation is predicated on optimism and belief, and these need regular injections of good news to keep them ticking over. I often think of the otter when I am in need of such a boost. Conservationists are fortified by the conviction that there is a formula to be followed, and that if it is adhered to, the dire state of nature will in due course be turned around. Otters are the embodiment of that belief: from the lowest and most pessimistic point in their fortunes in the late 1970s, a succession of measures, no one of which would work by itself, fell into place to bring the otter back from the brink. Protection from direct killing; scientific research that uncovered the impact of pesticides; control over the use of said pesticides; restoration of aquatic ecosystems; designation of the most important wetlands and river corridors as protected areas or Nitrate Vulnerable Zones;[10] catchment management planning....

But there must have been something else. The UK's wildlife has been in unremitting decline for decades;[11] the otter is both a wellspring of hope, and one of very few counter-currents to all the causes for despair. Let us not forget that less than a hundred years ago the otter was as unloved as all the other predatory animals that have innocently incurred our displeasure. Two books for successive generations changed that, perhaps exhuming some deeply-buried affinity that centuries of irrational fear and unwarranted intolerance had suppressed. If we are not to have to rebuild that affinity species by species, we must recognise attitude change as the vital underpinning of any technocratic formula. We need to treat the cultural dimension of conservation as seriously as we do our protected areas system or our pollution prevention goals. Then, perhaps, the good news of the otter's return may ripple across all nature, like a ring of bright water.

NINE

Nightingale

Field notes 20 April, 2019

Imagine the smell of birch smoke tangling with the
hyacinthine perfume of bluebell. It is the smell of late
afternoon. The flowers' scent has been washing the
day long through the rooky wood, as Shakespeare
might have called it – the smoky wood.[1] Smoky
with the haze of oak-burn from the charcoal-makers'
mounds and hazy with the lacustrine blue of the
flowers; and rook-chorused. Towards the day's end
logs are fetched from a pile built last autumn, and
a new fire made on the ashes of the one that died
slowly overnight. The sun has gone and the chill
has returned. We are grateful for the flame and the
ale, and the smell from the pot curling through the
birch-smoke and the bluebell-smoke; and curling on,
up along the moss of the boughs and up through the
half-furled leaves of the coppice hornbeams; higher

again, into the oaks and on into the free air and the sky: smoke, perfume and song alloyed into a lofting twist of some one thing, some ether.

I was standing under old coppiced hornbeams and tall oaks trying not to recite poetry. Instead I thought about the woodsmen and their families who wrote barely a line between them but who created and inhabited this human landscape we call ancient woodland: foresters, gamekeepers, woodwards, barkers, potash-makers and colliers – the charcoal-burners of old. I was in Kent by invitation, to think and write about nightingales. I tried to allow my mind the freedom to travel in time, unburdened by centuries of poetry, and to think of wood itself, and smoke, as the true tokens of the intervolved lives of people and nightingales.

For at least 2800 years poets from Persia to Greece and from Spain to England have been the self-appointed chroniclers of that relationship. Mark Cocker believes that the nightingale is "the single most important motif in all world poetry",[2] an argument he uses in railing against the impending loss of Britain's most important nightingale site, Lodge Hill near Rochester, home to 85 pairs. Cocker's anguish is well-founded. The UK has lost 90% of its nightingales since 1970, a cliff-edge fall in numbers that has been accompanied by a contraction into England's south-east corner. It once extended as far north as South Yorkshire and westwards into Wales. The last national survey took place in 2012 and revealed that only between 5,095 and 5,983 singing males remained.[3] Now Kent has become something it should never have been: The Nightingale County, and the nightingale is on its way to becoming something it should not be: the Bird of Kent, the bird of the county where I grew up. It's personal.

In May 2014 the folk singer Sam Lee performed *The Tan Yard Side* to the accompaniment of a nightingale live on BBC Radio 4, to mark the 90th anniversary of the first-ever outside broadcast. In 1924, against the advice of the BBC's Director-General Lord John Reith, programme-makers had staked the success of the venture on Surrey's nightingales cooperating in testing the new technology. They arrived at Oxted, home of the cellist Beatrice Harrison, having advertised throughout Britain the promise of a unique double-act. Harrison played while an unprecedented number of listeners, many of whom had no radio of their own and had been invited to huddle round their neighbours', waited for the birds to join her. For almost the whole programme, the birds remained silent as Harrison played piece after piece, from *Chant Hindu* to *The Londonderry Air*. The broadcasters prepared themselves for a dressing-down from Reith the following day. Then, fifteen minutes before the programme was scheduled to end, the first nightingale started to sing. By the end of the broadcast, the BBC had made history, and had created an immediate sensation with what was to become an annual live event for the next twelve years.

Following his modern-day reworking of this magical formula, Sam offered small groups the chance to experience and participate in music-making with nightingales. He and I had met once or twice before, but I wasn't expecting the email inviting Jane and me to join him for one of his 2019 *Singing with Nightingales* events. Looking down the list of venues, I noticed that one event was to be held on a small farm in Shadoxhurst, a village in Kent that I had never heard of. It turned out to be less than five miles from Boldshaves, home of the Wealden Literary Festival and the place that, coincidentally, I had also been invited to, to connect with nightingales.

Green Farm's owner, Martin Richmond-Coggan kept a bonfire stoked with birch and his partner MaryAnn served cans of beer and glasses of wine as the guests assembled. We were joined by a large, bearded man who wore sheepskin and carried a hazel staff and who had appeared unnoticed from the trees, like a vagrant wayfarer attracted by the smell of the stew which was simmering in a cast-iron pot over the fire. Corin Stuart turned out to be a member of Sam's company The Nest Collective, and is a naturalist, actor and storyteller. While the food was cooking, Corin and Sam led us out from the farm and into the woods owned by Martin and MaryAnn's neighbours, Mike and Jan Bax, to hear the evening chorus. Martin pointed out the flowers that carpeted much of the woodland floor. "It takes a hundred years for bluebells to colonise a wood and four hundred years for wood anemone, so we know these woods are at least as old as that." Corin explained that this is due to the gradual settling-in of the complex relationships between certain fungi and the woodland soil, itself a product of years of leaf-fall and an ever more complex invertebrate ecology.

Two blackbirds, two robins and two wrens maintained a constant background accompaniment to a soloing song thrush. Occasionally a blackcap interjected a free-form improvisation. An air-piercing chiffchaff counted half-second beats, pushing against a woodpigeon's laid-back Latin rhythm. A coarse shout from a pheasant, a descending riff from a chaffinch, the erotically pulsing courtship of stock doves. Distant sheep. Sam described the dawn and evening choruses as two waves of sound passing round the northern hemisphere as the Earth rotates. In time only the song thrush, always the last to finish, was left.

We returned to the bonfire, knowing that it would be some time before the nightingales would reach peak song. At ten-thirty, with a full moon to light our way, Sam having requested that torches be used only for emergencies, we re-entered the forest. The first nightingale was singing hundreds of yards away, and in silence we followed a track that led roughly in its direction. The multi-trunked hornbeams cast deep shadows, backlit by a large, full, fiery moon that glared sharply into eyes adjusted to the deep night of the forest. They seemed military and monstrous, like mythic forest guards. It was not hard to imagine what thoughts they would have conjured in a superstitious folk at a time when the nightingale would have sung against the howl of wolves.

As we drew closer to the bird, we became aware of others proclaiming their own tract of forest. Our nightingale showed no sign of having noticed our approach, although he must have known we were there; he sang loudly and continuously and continued after we had reached our chosen spot – some three yards away. Sam whispered that we were to settle into as comfortable a position as possible, sitting or standing as we wished. I stood, leaning against a birch trunk, from which spot I counted another five nightingales singing across the forest. The nearest bird paused not once as the group rustled the undergrowth before settling. He paused not once in forty minutes, singing mostly solo, but now and then Sam would sing too. Sam had invited a flautist, Paul Cheneour, who played an occasional improvised rippling melody, or imitated a phrase or two from the bird's infinite repertoire. The nightingale continued as we rose forty minutes later and rustled out of the scrub and lumbered back onto the track, and continued on, his song receding into the night as we returned to the clearing at Green Farm. The breadth of the nightingale's repertoire, and the volume of sound it produces, seems to us extraordinary. Nightingales have a collective catalogue of at least 1,160 different sounds. Compare this to two of their rivals as Britain's best-loved songster: 340 for skylarks and about 100 for blackbirds.[4] The nightingale's HVC, that part of the brain responsible for creating sound, is bigger than in most other birds: its capacity for song is not an idea that humans have conjured, it is a biological compulsion.

Between 77 AD and his death two years later in the volcanic eruption that destroyed Pompeii, Pliny the Elder compiled his *Natural History*. He wrote:

Nightingales pour out a ceaseless gush of song for fifteen days and nights on end when the buds of the leaves are swelling – a bird in no small measure remarkable. In the first place there is so loud a voice and so persistent a supply of breath in such a tiny little body; then there is the consummate knowledge of music in a single bird: the sound is given out with modulations, and now is drawn out into a long note with one continuous breath, now varied by managing the breath, now made staccato by checking it, or linked together by prolonging it, or carried on by holding it back; or it is suddenly lowered, and at times sinks into a mere murmur, loud, low, a bass, treble, with trills, with long notes, modulated when this seems good – soprano, mezzo, baritone; and briefly all the devices in that tiny throat which human science has devised with all the elaborate mechanism of the flute, so that there can be no doubt that this sweetness was foretold by a convincing omen when it made music on the lips of the infant Stesichorus. And that no one may doubt its being a matter of science, that the birds have several songs each, and not all the same but every bird songs of its own. They compete with one another, and there is clearly an animated rivalry between them.[5]

Recent research by Valentin Amrhein and his colleagues suggests that only unpaired males sing during the darkest hours of the night, whereas those that have secured mates only sing in the daytime, especially at dawn and dusk, to prevent incursions by other males.[6] Females arrive back from Africa later than the males, migrating mostly at night. One theory is that nocturnal singing is costly, given that the birds are otherwise diurnal, for example in their feeding habits, and that a male singing strongly at night is a sign of his prowess and quality as a mate and father.

♠

England and a sliver of Wales is the far north-west edge of the nightingale's natural world range. Britain and Ireland are at the far north-west edge of many species' range, but in most cases, this is a geological inevitability; there are 1876 miles of ocean before the next temperate land mass. But the nightingale has room to spare, being confined by climate to southern Britain. Its heartland is the land of hot, dry continental and Mediterranean summers and its winter home in West Africa. In 2007 a team of scientists investigated the relationship between Europe's breeding birds and its climate. For each species, they established the climate parameters that appeared to govern the bird's distri-bution, tested whether their models could correctly predict the birds' actual distribution; and when the model fitted the reality – for the nightingale the fit was near-perfect – they projected the birds' future distribution based on expected future climate change. The resulting map of the nightingale's late 21st century breeding range shows the species consolidating its (now former) sparse presence in Yorkshire, and expanding up the east coast into Northumberland and southern Scotland.[7] Climate change should see the nightingale spread into new areas, but the opposite is happening.

The population in Britain has been declining since at least the mid-1960s, probably due to a combination of factors including poorer woodland quality, pressures on migration and habitat degradation in their West African winter quarters. Whatever the reasons, the effect is shocking, with over 90% of our nightingale population lost in two human generations.

Coppicing trees is what kept people and nightingales together in Britain. Cutting them down to ground level every 15 to 20 years and allowing them to regrow created a valuable and renewable resource of building material, fuel, leather-tanning products, fencing and forage. The trees may be very ancient below ground, where their centuries-old roots and the soil ecology they support bring health and stability to the whole forest, but above ground the same trees are young and vigorous. Sometime in the Neolithic we discovered the secret of eternal youth for trees. We kept some trees uncut to become venerable ancients, or as a long-term source of timber for the ships, great halls and cathedrals of a distant future. This pattern of coppice-with-standards created a mixture of damp, shady areas under the tall trees and dense tangles of bramble and honeysuckle where the light was allowed in. The ancient oaks and their unique lichens and fungi invited in thousands of different specialist beetles, snails, wasps, flies, spiders, millipedes and woodlice. The youthful hornbeams fed hundreds of different types of moths and butterflies, sawflies and hoverflies. The damp shade hosted yellow archangel, primrose, bluebell and wood anemone; the bright glades in the new coppice were temporary jousting-fields for perpetually skirmishing speckled wood and silver-washed fritillary butterflies. Then, within a few years of the cut, the undertangle would return, the butterflies would move on and the nightingales would move in. Over time the canopy would close out the light, the ground layer would thin, and the nightingale territories would shift into more recently-coppiced plots, known since Norman times as *coupes*.

The earliest evidence for coppicing comes from the trackways of oak, ash and lime built across the peat of the Somerset Levels. They were constructed from small trees and poles cut on both short and long rotations and, thanks to the science of dendrochronology, can be dated precisely to 3806 BCE. Four millennia later the Romans arrived and set about coppicing large tracts of the Wealden woodlands to fuel their iron works. The new cross-channel polity saw the population of Kent increase dramatically as did the demand for forest produce, which in turn drove up the value of woodland. Woods were settled and fragmented, but also better managed as a sustainable resource. Widespread settlement of the common wooded land began in the 7th century, when the Jutish herdsmen of east Kent who had been using the woods seasonally for pannage and pasturage gradually established the scattered villages and small towns of the Weald.[8]

The eventual decline in coppicing was less extreme in Kent than elsewhere in the country due to a sustained local demand for paper pulp and pitwood. When I was growing up, paper-making was one of Kent's characteristic industries. One of the largest and one of the few surviving companies, Swantex (now Swan Mill), still operates in my home town of Swanley, which owes its name to the ancient practice of pannage – the turning out of swine into woodland clearings or *leys*.

Coppicing is still practiced. Nowhere is it an economically viable industry in the old way: no essential product of the woods can be produced that is more effective, easier to produce, cheaper to process and more convenient to transport than its modern equivalent. Fossil fuels have replaced wood and charcoal, hopefully to be replaced in turn; plantation conifer, concrete and steel have replaced oak beams, synthetic tannin has replaced bark, mined potassium chloride has replaced potash. Imported goods replaced everything, whether they came by ship from the other side of the world or by rail from a cheaper source at the other end of the county. Now, coppicing happens where people want it to happen and are prepared to bear the cost and inconvenience of using wood over plastic, charcoal over oil, local charcoal over imported charcoal. Or they want to revive the old skills of wood-turning and stave-making. Enthusiasts cut wood, wait for it to season, stack it in mounds, fire it and wait again. In clearings they build pizza ovens for when the charcoal is ready.

The economics of it are the economics of lifestyle choice, not of necessity. Except, that coppice woodland is a unique and rich habitat for wildlife, and subsidised conservation has introduced new rules of economics.

In her book *Wilding*, Isabella Tree described her experience of letting Knepp Castle, the Estate she runs with her husband Charlie Burrell, run wild. Burrell's family has owned its 3,500 acres of heavy Wealden clay since 1787. After exactly 200 years, Sir Charles inherited the land and a failing farm business, which he modernised at considerable capital cost. Despite the investments, during the fifteen years to 2002 it suffered an operating loss in thirteen of them. Led by what Tree describes as "an amateurish love for wildlife and because we would have lost an impossible amount of money if we had continued to farm" they re-thought the business, and informed DEFRA[9] of their intention to "establish a biodiverse wilderness in the Low Weald of West Sussex". The project started simply, by leaving fields in the southern part of the estate to lie fallow – the less productive ones at first, then over four years progressively leaving the whole southern block unfarmed. From the beginning of 2010 the whole estate was entered into Higher Level Stewardship, the UK government scheme that, under the auspices of the EU agri-environment programme, grants payments for every hectare or linear metre of wildlife-friendly habitat created.[10]

The Burrells' vision included introducing large herbivores and letting them roam free. Dozens of English Longhorn cattle, Exmoor ponies and fallow deer were introduced along with

Tamworth pigs. The Knepp reach of the river Adur was reengineered under an agreement with the Environment Agency, freeing it from its heavily canalised, tax-payer maintained straightjacket and granting it the freedom of its floodplain.

Naturalists descended to help monitor progress, eventually recording thirteen of Britain's seventeen bat species, and charting the arrival of purple emperor butterflies and turtle doves. Nightingales seemed to have disappeared, in line with the catastrophic national trend, but in 2012 researchers from Imperial College London recorded 34 territories. They had returned, and perhaps uniquely, were increasing in the face of the national decline.[11] *Wilding* has become a classic of contemporary conservation writing, inspiring other landowners to investigate the same radical rethink of their business and personal goals. In a chapter devoted to the species, Isabella Tree wonders where nightingales would have nested before people worked the forests and established the industries that support coppicing. She notes that the estate encompasses places with old names associated with this ancient practice, such as Lindfield Copse, Pollardshill and Alder Copse. Burrell and Tree didn't reinstate coppicing in order to bring back nightingales, rather the nightingales re-established themselves in areas where hedgerows were left unmanaged and in other areas where dense scrub had grown due to their benign neglect. Tree suggests that had the return of the nightingale been a specific aim, established conservation wisdom would have advocated re-establishing a managed coppice woodland, whereas by just leaving fields and their margins untended except by the unconstrained browsing of large herbivores, they have created the second most important nightingale site in England after Lodge Hill.

Any species that seems to depend on a habitat that owes its existence to human intervention begs the same fascinating question. Where did house martins nest before houses? Where did corncrakes crake before corn? If we can understand the primeval nightingale's life in truly natural habitat, we can refine the search for modern-day surrogates. What Tree and Burrell's experience confirmed, is the importance of large areas of dense scrub in an insect-rich environment. The abandoned former ordnance storage facility at Lodge Hill has scrubbed over through passive neglect, in much the same way that Knepp has done, in response to a policy of active neglect.

I pondered the question – what would the nightingale's pre-human habitat preferences have been? Scrub is as human in origin as coppice, the one a result of abandonment or neglect, the other a deliberate exploitation of the forest. For a time the human population of Britain was small enough to have had little impact on the wild wood. Some of that woodland would have been high, closed-canopy forest, but it is now thought that much of it would have been more savannah-like in structure. Primeval wildlife must have fallen into four categories. Some were species of the stable wilderness – habitats like old-growth forest, rocky coasts and islands. Others were species of unstable habitats like estuarine saltmarsh, able to shift location or fluctuate in abundance to the rhythm of natural change. There were species that inhabited very rare habitat like grassland, some of which were eventually destined to form close associations with the humans who created surrogate versions with their settled agriculture: birds like the skylark. In my unofficial classification, it seems likely that the nightingale falls into a fourth category, species who exploit sudden dramatic change – the irregular inflictions of storm, fire and flood visited upon a region to disrupt the equilibrium. Perhaps, then, the nightingale is indeed a species of old forest, moving in after a great storm or a lightning-strike and subsequent fire. Another possibility is that the greatest of all herbivores, mammoths, would have crashed through the forest in nomadic herds, coppicing the trees as they went.

Nightingales need dense scrub or woodland undertangle for nesting, bare ground for foraging and an abundant insect supply, so a diverse mixture of shrub species such as hawthorn, blackthorn, dog rose and bramble is best. Ancient woodland that has been damaged by storms or coppiced by people provides such a mosaic of features, as do large tracts of scrub on abandoned or untended land. Small areas of scrub and hedgerow embedded in intensive farmland does not suffice. There is good evidence that the recent rise in small deer numbers – of muntjac and roe – has been particularly detrimental by reducing the density of understorey vegetation.[12] Martin Richmond-Coggan believes there is a link between Kent's relatively stable nightingale population and the relatively slow arrival of muntjac across the county.

A few days later I returned to Kent, to keep my appointment at Boldshaves, home to Peregrine Massey, a former High Sheriff of Kent and his wife Dee. Their daughter Laura Willan runs the Wealden Literary Festival in the open gardens there with her husband Andrew. They invited me to make a visit in the spring to get to know the site's nightingales, and to return in the June to share my thoughts and early writings with the Festival audience. I began by reading the 'field notes' from Shadoxhurst that begin this essay. Then I introduced more field notes, from Boldshaves itself.

Field notes, 25 April 2019

> The nightingale's season is the season of soft
> leafing-up. The tops of the trees report the wind's
> strength, a moderate breeze, but the noise of it is
> slight; leaves are at a soft, unripe stage, yielding to
> the wind more quietly when compared to the older
> leaves' noisy resistance (and also compared to winter's

bare twigs). The leaves treat sunlight in much the same, soft-handed way. More translucent than older leaves, also more shiny, so some of the light from this low evening angle skates off the surface and the rest seeps through the leaf's fabric. Sound and light fall soft onto herb Robert, herb Bennett, dog's mercury, primrose, pendulous sedge.

Hawthorn pearled with closed- and half-budded may.

And its season is the time when ponds are scummed-over with tree pollen, catkin-frass and willow seed. And the brief time when the previous autumn's leaves are stimulated to release their last vapours by the slanting touch of the sun; the forest mixes them with the green-smell of the new spring foliage, and the feminine scent of bluebells.

During that April walk I took in a four-acre field that looked to have been cut into the wood as if scissored from a map, no doubt *assarted* in the early medieval period. I noticed a single wild service tree at the right-hand edge of the field where mostly the boundary was a canopy formed by the lowest branches of hornbeam. From this hem of young leaves hung a threadbare curtain of wafting silk: the droplines of winter moth caterpillars, minute and the same spring green as the unfurling leaves. The sun caught their light, and the breeze played silent arpeggios through their tethers, which lengthened slowly as the caterpillars played out more silk. Their meagre gravity did little to speed the descent, but their sideways flights, driven every minute or two by a gust of breeze, allowed the rapid release of more thread; or they snapped off and reached the grass that way. The strongest gusts brought them all down, and each time the breeze dropped again, a new wave of abseilers was launched.

It is one delicate fragment of the food-web that encompasses the nightingale, the pipistrelle, the sparrowhawk, the whole forest. Winter moth caterpillars emerge in early spring, after four or five days on which daytime high temperatures have reached 13 degrees Celsius or more. In 2007 Dr. Margriet van Asch of the Netherlands Institute of Ecology discovered that as spring temperatures now reach this level sooner than in past decades, some winter moth eggs hatch before the leaf buds have begun to open. Tree leaf burst is also getting earlier with climate change, but it is controlled by different factors, and the insect and the tree are shifting out of synch. However, winter moth hatch timing is genetically controlled, and the moths are evolving to resynchronise with the trees, delaying their response to the temperature trigger by between five and ten days.[13] Insectivorous birds, including the nightingale, are arriving and breeding earlier in response to the shifting timelines of the insects. Much besides the caterpillar hangs on the fine line of its silken thread: tree, moth and bird will need to keep track with each other's shifting phenologies for decades to come.[14]

I shared the festival stage with my friend Julian Hoffman, having decided that this final essay would be finished with the addition of his thoughts and those of the audience as we had a public conversation about nightingales in culture and conservation. Julian and I had been brought together by Laura because we had both been writing about nightingales and had independently identified the Wealden as the obvious place to do this. It is perhaps the only Literary Festival at which nightingales will be quietly (by late June) and invisibly going about the business of procreation within yards of event marquees, craft stands, refreshment stalls and a thousand assembled people. Julian's book *Irreplaceable* was newly published;[15] to write it he visited a selection of the most important and threatened places for wildlife in the world, and in each place he met local activists and set out to tell their stories. One such place was Lodge Hill, thirty miles from Boldshaves. We both saw it as the starkest reminder that even the country's most important site for one of its best-loved and most threatened birds was not immune from developers' voracious appetite for land. The story of Lodge Hill is simply another retelling of a story that had played out hundreds of times before. A site is given formal recognition as an SSSI for its national importance for wildlife. It enters the conservation psyche as a 'protected area' and we assume it is safe, only to be reminded that one thing the UK protected areas system lacks, is a single protected area. Someone has other ideas for using the land, in this case housing. The conservationists marshal their battle-hardened troops, oil their precision-honed arguments, unlock the war chest. Again.

Lodge Hill is not some beautiful hornbeam coppice with oak standards, managed in ways unaltered since Norman times. It is abandoned land, left to scrub over, former Ministry of Defence land, and they are trying to decommission the place. First, they need to clean up 140 years' worth of unexploded ordnance. Quietly, they have transferred the land to a quango, Homes England, so that the cost of the clean-up can be absorbed into the economics of developing thousands of houses. They are asking the nightingales to pay with their lives; routine for the MoD perhaps, but you could equally call it a bomb-threat.

If conservation wins this latest battle, some will say that it proves the system works. But it's a battle that has been raging since 2011 and like all the others, it is draining resources from conservation charities, business and government alike. Resources which should be invested in good development and great conservation. If it takes the best part of ten years to win no more than a reprieve, it proves the system is a failure. That's if we win.

Isabella Tree was in the audience, having earlier in the day taken part in a public debate about rewilding. After the talk, we discussed the challenge of maintaining nightingale habitat for the long term. "The problem with Lodge Hill is that it will only be good for nightingales for a time, then the scrub will give way to woodland. You'll need to get large herbivores in." She was referring to dry scrubland's natural tendency to act as a medium-term nurse crop for tall trees. 'The thorn is the mother of the oak' is an old New Forest saying, and an even older French one. It refers – unknowingly perhaps – to the work of the wood mouse as nature's forester who in autumn caches acorns under the leaf-litter, protected by brambles impenetrable to larger animals. There is a long-held traditional view that it is jays and squirrels who help in the regeneration of oaks, through their habit of burying hundreds of acorns for safe-keeping through the winter, always forgetting where a few are hidden. But research suggests that that both species are capable of remembering almost every last one. This may also be true of mice, if they live long enough; but a mouse's febrile life often ends abruptly. While some may live to retrieve all their treasure in the course of the winter, others will leave a legacy, one that takes root the following spring and two or three years later emerges into the light from within the tangle of thorn. Left to its own devices, a grove of maturing trees will shade out the scrub. Norman foresters understood this, and prevented over-exploitation of bramble, blackthorn and hawthorn scrub as an essential element of long-term forest management. In recent times, however, scrub has become regarded as useless, inconvenient and unsightly.

Which is why we are now waging the fourth battle of Lodge Hill. The first took place between October 2011 and November 2013, ending when Medway Council withdrew its housing strategy, which RSPB had objected to as it would have entailed building 5000 homes on prime nightingale habitat. Despite this, the Ministry of Defence's developers reapplied with new documents just three months later, launching the second battle. Medway Council approved the application despite objections from the RSPB, Buglife, Butterfly Conservation, Kent Bat Group and Kent Wildlife Trust. The second battle raged for three and a half years, ending when the application was withdrawn, to avoid a costly Public Inquiry that the MoD and Medway Council judged they would probably lose. A new proposal for 2000 homes on the site, submitted by the government agency Homes England, who had been quietly granted the land by the MoD, saw the fight for Britain's most important nightingale haven renewed just six months later.

The brief third battle ended in December 2018 when Homes England announced that it was withdrawing the 2000 homes proposal and that it would bring a smaller 500-home scheme forward, none of which would be built directly on the SSSI. Conservation groups have given this a cautious welcome, but fear the development will directly abut the boundary, with impacts that could still be hugely damaging for the nightingale population.

"People immediately think cats, but noise, lighting, dog walking, recreational pressure are all a factor", my colleague Adrian Thomas, the RSPB's Campaign Manager in South East England, told me. "And we await the next iteration of Medway's local plan later in the summer, which we expect to include 12,000 more houses elsewhere on the Hoo Peninsula, many within 400m of the SSSI, the distance at which we think these impacts are likely to have an effect. It's a major concern that the SSSI will get ringed with multiple developments."

Lodge Hill and Knepp represent two crossing pathways along which place-based conservation is travelling. Lodge Hill, supposedly protected by its status as an SSSI, reminds us that the UK's protected area system is at the mercy of the development planning process and as such is subordinate to it. It is a system that has failed some of the most important and precious places in the past, and which every year continues to see damage or neglect inflicted on others. At best the struggle to defend the most important wildlife sites from development is a continual conveyor belt of costly and divisive cases, which can be comprehensively lost but never conclusively won. It is a 70-year old tool[16] that has rusted in the hands of conservationists who continue to wield it for want of a modern implement, with no choice but to participate in an unfit system.

Knepp has no official place in the country's gazette of important areas for wildlife. The wilding of Knepp has its origins in the dysfunctional tangle of public policies and payment systems that failed the Burrell farm business as it has thousands of other family farms over the decades. There is nothing currently in farming policy or funding that makes wilding happen; it is not part of the toolkit that conservationists can deploy with any strategic support from the public sector. It is dependent on rare initiatives by farmers seeking to repurpose their business, on a few instances of private landscape-scale projects run by billionaire philanthropists, or on occasional partnerships of landowning bodies intent on experimenting with their own solutions.

As for the nightingale, no species exhibits a greater gap between the universal high regard in which it is held and our inability to prevent it being lost from Britain. It illustrates better than any other co-habitant of this land that our relationship with the rest of the natural world is crumbling and the conservation model on which I have built a career and on which a nation pins its hopes is failing. In part 2 I set out the case for the radical and urgent rethink that nature needs.

Landscapes of Change

TEN

Vanishing Points

In the Fen Country

Every spring from the first spring I can remember until my fifteenth, my father stopped the car by the side of the Wisbech road so that he and I could walk into the adjacent field and look for lapwings' eggs. It was the most ancient of Fenland traditions. He called them plovers, and every time we travelled to the land where he grew up, that name and his accent returned. In the early sixties, not many cars passed that way. Bikes, yes: pedalled slowly by farm workers in flat caps and wool jackets, with their knees splayed out in the Fenland manner.

Exchanging gifts of eggs in spring was a Saxon thing, and when the country converted, it became an Easter tradition. The richest and tastiest eggs were lapwings', and when Easter fell at the right time, Fenland boys could collect fresh ones from incomplete clutches for the market at Wisbech. Dad was

213

born the year after the Lapwing Act of 1926 put a stop to the worst ravages of commercial egging; but before he left the Fens for National Service and then a life in London and Kent, he maybe collected a few. Mostly, though, there was no need. My grandfather Arthur was a foreman on the farm, and through the Depression years and the War years, when other people of their class might have struggled, grandmother Lily's table had food on it. Except when Arthur did his back in: then the economics of the farm were brutal. Unable to work, no pay. And no state welfare. Uncle Walter and Uncle Herbert were old enough to earn a little, but hens' eggs and vegetables from the garden became the mainstay. When the cat brought a blackbird in, my father saw his mother pluck it for the stew.

Not that we were in that field to steal eggs. We just loved birds, and we enjoyed the aerobatics and the sound of the lapwings mustering to attack. When we found a nest, we spent a few seconds admiring its simple and profound beauty before backing away.

The one question I never asked my father, and never thought to until it was too late, was the obvious one – did he miss the Fens? He never betrayed signs of it, but as I grew up I knew it was his deep connection to nature that I had inherited. The Fens of his youth were not the Fens of mediaeval times, echoing to the voices of cranes. Nor are the Fens of today remotely similar to the landscape he grew up in in the 1930s, and they bear little resemblance to the Fens I remember from the 1970s.

There is a tract of land between Boston, Bourne, March and King's Lynn, nearly 800 square miles of it, that appears virtually devoid of non-human life, an impression not helped by the unrelieved flatness. At the centre of what is today an agri-industrial wasteland, the village of Sutton St. James is where my father was born. Stretched like a canvas on which would once have been daubed meanders and ox-bows, hayfields and ancient pastures bounded by lines of osier, a backdrop for the ripples and eddies of skylark song, now the landscape is an unrelenting, roller-painted green. As for the skylarks, a verse from Shelley's ode comes to mind:

We look before and after,
And pine for what is not:
Our sincerest laughter
With some pain is fraught;
Our sweetest songs are those that tell of saddest
thought.[1]

Conservationists will use terms like 'denatured' for cases such as this, as in: The UK is the 29th most denatured country in the world. This precise assessment is based on a scientific measure called the biodiversity intactness index.[2,3] If the UK ranks 29th out of 218 countries on the list, then to balance the relatively intact natural beauty of the Hebrides, say, there must be places in Britain that are close to the very top of that league of shame.

To denature a tract so great is to dehumanise it. The Lincolnshire coastline, particularly the towns of Skegness and Mablethorpe, are among the most deprived ten percent of neighbourhoods in the country. That is no great surprise, but as the assessors of the 2015 Indices of Multiple Deprivation[4] noted, the parishes of the wider countryside in the hinterland are within the most deprived 30 percent which, for a rural area, is unusual. The wealth is there, in the form of large landholdings generating high subsidy revenue alongside the high-yield production revenue. Family farms have been taken over by large agribusinesses, typified by extensive fields, often managed by external contractors, maintained as near-perfect monocultures by high inputs of pesticides and fertilizers.[5] The landscape produces more food more cheaply than ever, but is largely inhospitable to wildlife and provides employment for very few people.

My father left the farming life in 1946, since when the UK has lost 150,000 miles of hedgerow, 50% of its downland, 98% of wildflower meadows and 50% of ancient woodlands, along with over 130,000[6] small farms, farmers and farming families.

Re:Connecting

Our species evolved in the savannahs of Africa over 200,000 years ago. All human life was played out in landscapes that often gave generously of their bounty but could be brutal at times of drought or wildfire, and dangers lurked throughout their grasslands, woods and marshes. Like all wildlife, this new species was adapted to thrive in the niche for which evolution had equipped it. It knew how to work the habitat, sense opportunity and danger, read the clouds, plan seasons ahead so that the fruits of one assuaged the privations of another. Two hundred millennia later it had conquered the globe, altered the meaning of time and distance, re-niched its ecology over and over again, and continually tinkered with a machine, Planet Earth, that it didn't understand and could never hope to control. Eventually it found itself in an increasingly uncomfortable alternative world of its own. At some point, with typical abstract ingenuity, it started to devote some of its intellectual potency to the study of its own well-being, finding that humanity had been shaped both cognitively and emotionally through those early interactions with the natural world of which it was once part.[7]

To this, some psychologists ascribe our apparent emotional bond with nature, extending perhaps even to a reverence that incorporates awe and wonder, and a love for life and all its complexity.[8] If so, then for this ancient relationship to so readily fall into disrepair would seem to be at odds. Whatever the reality of any innate bond between people and nature, it is beyond doubt that increased urbanisation and addiction to technology has weakened our drive to connect with it.

Studies have repeatedly shown our connectedness to nature in sharp decline. At least in anthropocentric western societies, this risks removing any meaning from nature, translating into a loss of respect for the natural world and indifference to environmental damage.

Yet there is a considerable body of hard evidence for the positive impact on people of reconnecting to nature. Hospital patients have been shown to get better quicker if the view from their beds includes natural features like trees.[9] Mental well-being improves with time spent in green space, to the extent that many physicians now routinely prescribe it.[10] It is surely self-evident that in our time, the benefits flow in both directions: the future of nature depends on it being valued by the people with the capacity to destroy it and the power to save it; rebuilding society's connectedness to nature is an urgent matter.

Most conservation organisations, including the RSPB, have responded by investing in the capacity to do more of what they have always been good at – creating opportunities for people to see and learn about wildlife on nature reserves and in local green spaces. Sharing enthusiasm and knowledge about wildlife is where my career began, and as I took on more senior responsibilities, I ensured that my teams built more people-facing work into all our conservation programmes. My philosophy was straightforward – my colleagues and I were all deeply connected to nature, were inspired, uplifted and awed by it. It was surely just a matter of giving others first-hand experience of what we believed they were missing out on.

It was several years before anyone seriously asked the question: what actually makes people feel connected to nature?

Miles Richardson, a psychologist who heads up a programme of research into nature connectedness at the University of Derby was among the first to do so.[11] In 2017 I was at the conference where Miles presented his findings and amidst all the explanation of methodologies, assumptions and analysis, one statistic stood out. As it appeared on the screen I noticed the heads of the 150 delegates in the room bowing in unison as they dutifully jotted it into their notebooks, before sitting up again to await the next notable snippet. The audience was drawn from across the spectrum of interested parties: social science researchers and students, local authority rangers, outdoor educators, policy-makers from Natural England, Natural Resources Wales, Scottish Natural Heritage and Department of the Environment Northern Ireland; along with numerous NGO practitioners and managers like me. It appears I made no note at the time, but I remember staring at the screen as the information it conveyed etched itself onto my memory.

Miles and his team of researchers had spent three years examining the factors that determined whether people came away from an experience with nature feeling more connected than before. A mere two percent reported that their connectedness had improved as a result of their having garnered facts, figures, knowledge and identification skills. My mind raced across all the instances I could recall from among the thousands of examples of 'interpretation' I had seen, and in many cases had created or approved. From information boards and guided walks on reserves to city-centre peregrine watches, the emphasis was on getting facts across as the first step in a 'journey' (a word that appears in countless strategies across the sector, and that suddenly seemed only to verbalise a redundant linearity of thought).

By contrast, five other types of experience were strong predictors of connection, accounting for 69 percent of improvements. While Miles's own word 'pathways' can also imply a line followed to a destination, I knew that here were vital new insights to help explain the decades-worth of cultural distancing I have been trying to document in this book. Perhaps, even, to guide the rebuild of a new cultural settlement between humanity and the rest of nature. It all boiled down to a simple table:

PATHWAY	DEFINITION
Contact	The act of engaging with nature through the senses
Beauty	The perception of aesthetic qualities including shape, colour and form that please the senses
Meaning	Using nature or natural symbolism to communicate a concept that is not directly expressed
Emotion	An affective state or sensation that occurs as a result of engaging with nature
Compassion	Extending the self to include nature, leading to a concern for other natural entities that motivates understanding and helping/co-operation

The Indian novelist and environmental author Amitav Ghosh, answering his own question: "how do we make sense of the Earth when it seems to be turning against us in revenge for its despoliation?" said that the very act of writing about the devastation can sometimes create a kind of coherence.[12] I started compiling notes for this book in 2017 and drafted the first few essays the following year. After another year, I found myself trying to reconcile two contrasting moods. On the one hand, 2019 was a time when to be a UK citizen had never seemed more difficult. Europeans and environmentalists, two overlapping communities with which I and millions of others identify, viewed the spectacle of our unprecedentedly inept political leadership – inside and outside government and inside and outside the UK – with disbelief and horror. On the other hand, strip away the traditional notions of what politics is, and the leadership was there, in the shape of hundreds of thousands of unenfranchised schoolchildren striking to hold my generation to account for failing theirs.

Are these the same young people whose disconnection from nature we have all lamented and so far failed to cure, or an elite group who have managed to remain in touch with the real world? For two decades I have considered the progressive distancing of people from their natural environment – now well into its second generation – as the greatest threat to any possibility of restoring a mutually-beneficial relationship between people and the rest of nature.

Much as I hope for an eventual turnaround in this alarming trend, for many more people to become much better nature-connected, Greta Thunberg and her millions of friends may have called it right. A more fundamental problem is intergenerational injustice. It has been around for ever, probably, but social media hasn't. Those of us who belong to one of the past three generations who have failed nature, and have therefore failed perhaps three generations to come, must atone by stepping out of their way, and amplifying their voices at every opportunity.

Because conservation – success or failure – is cultural. Unfortunately, culture change isn't something that organisations can just switch on – still less prescribe. But we can hope for a few things as successive cohorts of young people bring their influence to bear. In early 2019 I said as much at a conference in York.[13] It was an early opportunity to test some thoughts about the cultural dimension to conservation, and I offered this list of the changes that I hoped we could bring about:

- **Stop normalising loss**. 'The fundamental drivers of further loss are all intact' says Mark Cocker in *Our Place*.[14] I go further: loss is even built-in to our current conservation toolkit. We have knowingly deployed agri-environment schemes that are inadequate for arresting the decline of farmland birds, as the principal measure – essentially the only available measure – for the purpose. And our protected areas network depends on our winning every single battle for their continued protection under a planning system designed to promote development; otherwise continuous biodiversity loss at some rate becomes inevitable. So...

- **Protection must mean protection**. Does that mean that a protected area remains protected under all conceivable circumstances? No, but the vague presumption of protection that comes with SSSI status must be far harder to subvert. Such presumption lasts only until the next planning application, which triggers a process in which the possibility of loss is very real; and anyone can submit one at any time. If protection could only be lifted by an Act of Parliament, it would both democratise the fate of our protected areas and filter out all but those few proposals that genuinely represent an overriding public interest.

- **We must reboot our relationship with other species**. The casual use of prejudicial language like 'vermin' must be eliminated from polite discourse, so as to avoid demonising species that may occasionally – or even frequently – cause us inconvenience. We must become more tolerant of occasional depredations of our private interests by wild animals and embrace coexistence. If we are prepared to distort science to

221

justify killing hundreds of thousands of badgers[15] when more effective measures to protect cattle from bovine TB can be deployed, we should not be surprised when schemes like the pro-hunting, anti-conservation hen harrier brood management plan (see p. 9) become official policy. Speaking of which...

- **We must stop privileging hunting over conservation.** Intensive land management that is detrimental to wildlife and ecosystems, releasing millions of non-native pheasants for shooting, intensive prophylactic predator control, and manipulation of threatened species populations are all wrong. Furthermore, we all have the legal right to kill wild animals for sport, with no limit as to intensity, no need to show any public interest, and no possibility of that right being revoked. Whatever the morality of hunting, the modern-day voracity with which it is practiced is at odds with rebalancing our relationship with the natural world. If it is not to be outlawed altogether, the right to shoot wildlife must be conditional on its being demonstrably part of a beneficial programme of management of land and its natural wealth.

- **We need a culture of duty-led land ownership not privilege-led land ownership**. Land may be privately owned, and the owners may enjoy its benefits and privileges, but functionally it is part of the nation's natural asset base. We must replace farm subsidies with investments in land as a national asset. Abusive land management practices that the rest of us pay for (through subsidy, or loss due to flooding, or loss of natural capital such as soil or woodland) must stop. So we must...

- **Rethink our relationship with land**. Make all public land, Crown land, Royal Family property, National Nature Reserves and National Parks work as national assets and not (only) private assets. National Parks in particular are among the most nature-depleted tracts

222

in the UK, compared to how they should be, so we should start there, where options such as wilding must be embraced and fully favourable SSSI condition must be a minimum standard across the whole. And finally, and most importantly …

- **Votes at 15**.

I stand by all that, but even as I was speaking, I felt I hadn't quite nailed it. Conservation is all about optimism, and instilling hope. The causes for pessimism and despair are legion; are they outweighed by the causes for optimism and hope? If it were purely a matter of confronting the persistent drivers of loss with ever more sophisticated technocratic solutions, we would have begun to turn the plight of our wildlife around years ago. If it also takes persuasion that protecting and enhancing our natural environment makes sound economic sense, we have got off to a good start. The case for nature's role in making society happier and healthier, mentally and physically, seems unassailable, even without the tragedy of a pandemic to prove it. So why aren't we there yet?

Extinction Rebellion and the children's climate strikes are dismissed in certain sections of the media with language like 'doomsday cult' to describe XR and routine condescension (frequently descending into ageist, sexist bullying) reserved for Greta Thunberg. Both are portrayed as disproportionately influential on account of the reality-distorting effect of social media, and invariably characterised as bourgeois, especially by the bourgeois. It is difficult to know how close either side comes to representing a majority sentiment, but what is patently clear is that there *are* sides: there is a divide. It is surely the case that the birthplace and timing of Extinction Rebellion – in Britain, contemporaneously with Brexit – is explained by the two-dimensional divisionist politics of our times. Dysfunctional political institutions are no place to find solutions to complex, global crises of any kind (Covid-19 will test this assertion while this book is on the printing presses); meantime it is for 'rebels' to work across the traditional boundaries of age, class and party allegiance and to listen beneath and beyond inflammatory rhetoric.

Mainstream conservation organisations find themselves on new, unfirm ground. On one side, we have to deal with the people who run things day-to-day, and work what is sometimes called the 'inside track' – close enough to the decision-makers that we can be trusted influencers. This is where dispassionate adherence to analytical rigour comes into its own. The 'rebels' also cite The Science but then quickly go on to use it to explain their anger and their fear, the twin engines of their emotional power. Can we deploy both to make change happen in a way that is both orderly and urgent? Perhaps we can draw inspiration from recent precedents: from #MeToo to plastic-shaming, ingrained cultures are showing themselves capable of shifting.

I have already quoted Eli Enns. He is a member of Vancouver Island's Nuu-chah-nulth nation and a political scientist working in constitutional law and ecological governance. When he states that western knowledge sees the world in pieces in order to profit from it,[16] it is a straight-forward reiteration of the principles René Descartes set out in 1637.[17] Descartes was hugely influential in shaping modern conceptions of science in Western society, not least the exploitative relationship we have with nature, and the role of science in serving profit. It would be a mistake for conser-vation to continue to respond to nature's despoliation with a similarly disjointed view of the issues that cause it. Enns's view, that indigenous knowledge is more about understanding the interconnectedness of things, is not without parallel in recent western thought, however.

Dr Fritjof Capra,[18] a physicist and systems theorist, believes that what he calls the systems view of life requires a new kind of thinking — thinking in terms of relationships, patterns, and context. In science this is known as systems thinking. He points out that many indigenous cultures embody profound ecological awareness and describe nature in terms of relationships and patterns they discern and may explain in ways very different to us – through stories and art, for example.

Perhaps western conservation thinking needs to shrug off its linear, Cartesian procedural from time to time. Capra contends that energy, environment, climate change, economic inequality, violence and war cannot be understood in isolation. Instead of taking into account the interconnectedness of our biggest problems, so-called 'solutions' tend to focus on a single issue, thereby simply shifting the problem to another part of the system — for example, by producing more energy at the expense of biodiversity.

Another way of expressing it is in terms of Ecological Design – "a process in which our human purposes are carefully meshed with the larger patterns and flows of the natural world", in the words of U.S. environmentalist Prof. David Orr.[19] It requires a fundamental shift in our attitude towards nature, a shift from finding out what we can take from nature, to understanding what we can learn from her.

Orr's Ecological Design is an eloquent paraphrase of my personal definition of conservation: *rebuilding a mutually-beneficial relationship between people and the rest of nature.*

Satish Kumar, the Rajasthan-born co-founder of the ecology-centred Schumacher College at Dartington Hall, Devon, goes further still. He defines three 'Ecologies': Shallow Ecology considers nature conservation important, but only because nature is useful to people. We take care of the environment so that we can benefit from nature for a long time to come. For the advocates of Deep Ecology, nature has intrinsic value. Trees are good, not just because they are useful to humans, giving us oxygen, taking our carbon or providing shade, fruit, and wood: trees are good in themselves. Kumar himself calls for a mutually beneficial and unconditional coexistence in what he calls Reverential Ecology. This states that we do not need to master nature or steward it: we can be participants in it and co-creators of it, as an integral expression and extension of self. "With Reverential Ecology, all our narrow, petty disconnections disappear."

I went to India.

ELEVEN

From Stones to Humankind

Mumbai

Not long after sunset, during the brief tropical twilight, Krishna Tiwari and I looked down from the eastern flank of the Yeoor hills. We scanned over the darkening forest, across the low roofs of the slum district of Hanumanagar and over to the high-rise apartments and offices of Thane and east Mumbai. Lights were going on across the city, gradually at first, like the earliest, brightest stars at dusk, then suddenly the city was a Milky Way that streaked across the space between the black forest below us and the slaty sky with its moon before us.

We had climbed a stony track to reach a point half way up the mountain: above us were the sacred twin peaks of Bhanja and Mama, whose craggy summits bit into the haze at 1181 feet and 1312 feet respectively. Behind us a natural rock platform of about half an acre had been levelled further, surfaced with pressed earth, partially cleared of trees, and fringed with beds of ornamental plants that merged into the surrounding forest. Silk flags rippled in a far corner of the plot, where another canopy shaded a mound that was covered in green and gold silk fabric. It was a Muslim shrine built into the forest, known as Mastan Darbar.

The nearly-full moon must have appeared from over the eastern horizon at about the same time that Krishna was parking his Honda Unicorn by the wall that separates Hanumanagar from the forest. Unlike some of our rides during the previous five days, this one was short, about ten minutes from my hotel. We climbed through the heat and humidity of the late afternoon with our backs to the moon as it climbed with its face to the hills, so that by the time we reached the platform and turned to look down at the city we had left behind, we and the moon faced each other at eye level. In the shadow of Bhanja and Mama the city grew dark ahead of the sky, which was lightly veiled behind a diaphanous urban haze. Krishna and I moved to the edge of the platform, where we were to record an interview, and began another conversation about Mumbai's urban leopards, the last of the many I had had during the week. Krishna himself had arranged them all: touching stories from people of the Warli and Kokna tribes living in the forest itself, whose lives and those of the leopards are inextricable.

"Right now we are inside one of the largest protected urban forests in the world, with the highest density of leopards in the world."

A sudden night had come and the moon, from its low position, cast little light into the forest. We continued our conversation as we made our way down the hill and back towards Hanumanagar. Krishna was happy to navigate the steep, twisting, rocky path by any moonlight that filtered through to the ground, but I decided I needed the help of my head torch. We had not descended far when, as I lifted my head to light the way forward, the beam reflected back two cats' eyes, like stationary fireflies against the black of the forest.

There was something familiar about the way the animal moved its head: differing only in size, it had all the disinterested poise of a domestic cat; somehow that was evident just by seeing its eyes. For a while it just stared back. From the little I could make out of the lie of the land, it was lying low to the ground about thirty yards ahead of us, at the left hand edge of the path. I whispered to Krishna, trying to get him to look along the line of my torch beam, as he struggled at first to see what I could see.

"Ahhh! Oohh, oh! It's a leopaaard...." Krishna's half-whispered first seven syllables had a pitch and rhythm like the first line of a football anthem, first rising, then falling. "So finally we saw a leopard. It seems to be moving." The two lights moved in a smooth, level motion, a few feet to the right.

"So what's our strategy? It's on the path, we've got to walk down this path..."

"No problem."

"Just keep going? Okay..."

"We'll keep our eye on it."

"I don't see it now, I think it moved to the right."

"It didn't seem to move far, it's somewhere here," said Krishna. I swept the path and the shroud of vegetation along its edges with my torch beam, but the eye-shine had gone. The leopard had slunk silently into the forest, or was perhaps simply looking away from us. "I have known these animals in this peripheral forest area for many years. They are very inquisitive and bold, they come to see what you're up to in their territory, but they never, ever get too close."

It never crossed my mind that we were in any danger; I had spent the past week talking with people for whom even closer encounters are an everyday probability. As Krishna explained, most people walk down from Mastan Darbar with nothing more than a mobile phone torch aimed at their feet. They never know when, and how often, they pass within feet of the forest's apex predator.

The Sanjay Gandhi National Park – universally referred to as 'SGNP' – is 104 km^2 of forested hills tucked into the cleft of the V-shaped city. It is an extension of the Western Ghats, the mountains that run for almost a thousand miles along India's west coast. Four days earlier, Krishna had picked me up from my hotel and I spent almost an hour on the pillion of his Unicorn, sweeping between lorries, cars and rickshaws; finally turning through the Borivali gate, into the forest for a couple of miles, and then a hundred yards or so along a dirt track before it petered out to a narrow footpath. We parked the bike and walked on through the forest until we came to a small river, the Dahisar, whose shallow ravine we crossed via the foot-wide lip of a concrete flood retention dam. Once across, we re-entered the trees between two shacks made from corrugated metal sheets and roofed with tarpaulins tied down over rough joists. It was the entrance to Chunapada, one of many scattered forest hamlets inhabited by 'tribals' – in this case the Warli people.

At the threshold of one doorway sat a middle-aged woman in a two-tone purple print dress with white, hand-printed circular motifs. Krishna addressed her warmly and she returned his greeting similarly, before welcoming me and fetching us each a plastic chair from inside the shack. Through Krishna, she introduced herself as Resha Satesh Kulkarni, and Krishna explained who I was and why I had come.

It was my first visit to a tribal *pada* and I had entered the hamlet with some trepidation, not knowing how I would be received, how trusting the people would be of my motives, how open to my questions they would be. Resha's relaxed smile helped me to relax, and over a cup of tea, we talked about life lived among the leopards, with Krishna as our interpreter.

"I have always lived here. I see a leopard every two or three days because this is a forest area and the leopard comes in search of water and food. I have seen leopards so many times that I am not scared; I know it has not come to harm me. Whenever anyone sees a leopard they shout, clap their hands, bang on the walls and the leopard goes away.

"My children are grown up and live away from the village. It's just me and my husband. It's my second marriage and my husband, who is not from this area, had no experience of leopards. One day soon after we got married he and my two children and I were visiting a village, Tumnipada, for a wedding. When we returned home there was a leopard sitting on a tree, hardly any distance away, as near as that pole." Resha pointed to a washing pole about eight feet away. "My husband was frightened; he had never seen a leopard before. But I am used to it, I know how to behave with the leopard, so I stood in front of my husband and put the children between us. The leopard jumped down right in front, had a look at us, and just walked away."

On the way back to the motorbike, Krishna explained that the known population of leopards in SGNP was 41, based on camera trap records that enabled a detailed scrutiny of their spot patterns, as individual as fingerprints.

"But there must be more like seventy," he said, "because we know there are leopards that stay in the forest and rarely come close to people, and others that simply haven't been caught on camera." Krishna started up the bike and I got on. "I'm taking you to another *pada* where a couple of years ago we captured footage of a leopard walking right by a house, past the doorway. Inside the house about two feet from the leopard you can see an old man asleep. He will be in his eighties, and I haven't been there for over a year, so I hope he's still around for you to meet him."

Patilpada was bordered on one side by the Chena river and on another by a mango plantation. Krishna introduced me to Kesan Musi, son of the old man Krishna had talked about, who was now in very poor health. In contrast to Resha, who appeared to enjoy recounting tales of forest life to a stranger, Kesan's answers had to be coaxed, again interpreted by Krishna.

"He just told me that last week only, a leopard took a cat from nearby," said Krishna. "Every day, before eight p.m., the leopard comes from this direction and just walks past by his house and crosses this path and goes to that village over there."

"When you were a very small child, were you ever scared of leopards?" I asked.

"No."

"When you saw the camera trap footage of the leopard close to your father sleeping, were you scared for your father?"

"He says 'no'", said Krishna. "You know, I know this guy. He is fearless, he goes into the forest with two other people at night – two, three o'clock in the morning to hunt, you know, unofficially, crabs and fish and small game..."

"When you go into the forest at night, do you see or hear leopards, and are your companions as fearless as you?"

"The person who roams in the forest has no fear."

"Do you have any stories about encounters with leopards, any interesting experiences or stories about someone else?"

"No."

"He has no fear so he has no stories to tell..." Krishna began, before interrupting himself. "Ah! *Now* he's talking about his fear... When there are *two* leopards, then...then he has fear. When there are two leopards, male and a female, and they are mating, when they hear a human sound, they get *frustrated*. I have a very beautiful instance of this myself. One day I was patrolling with the forest guards, and I guess those leopards were mating, and we disturbed them. They *growled* like anything, made a *horrific growling*, you know? I have experienced this twice in my life so I think he's right on this matter, they cannot tolerate being disturbed and they get very *ferocious*, you know?... He says that if at all anyone comes to know in the village that there are *two* leopards, and they are making sounds, so nobody comes out of the house, as they are very ferocious and they can attack people."

The trusting, tolerant, even affectionate terms in which local people described their relationship with the leopard was touching, but at the same time hardly believable. I wondered if there was another side to the story, and got my answer later that evening when Krishna emailed me various reports. One focused on the permanent residents of SGNP, living in the *padas*. It set out proposals for reducing leopard attacks on people during the time they are most at risk: squatting to relieve themselves in the forest during the monsoon, when the vegetation is thick and leopard and human encounter each other by surprise. The settlements may have been there for decades, but they were technically illegal, so building toilets is illegal, too. Krishna has proposed temporary structures for the three months of the monsoon only, but has met with little enthusiasm from the authorities.

The report included a table that set out annual casualty figures, covering the years between 2001 and 2007, and they made alarming reading. In 2001, there were five non-fatal injuries. The following year, 17 deaths and 8 injuries. In 2003 the number of incidents increased again, to 29, of which 14 were fatal; 2004 saw 30 incidents involving 19 fatalities. During three years in and around SGNP 64 people lost their lives to leopards and another 34 were hurt. Then the rate dropped sharply: over the following three years seven people died and seven more were injured. Two things didn't stack up – the strange pattern by which Mumbaikars had suffered a few years of appalling bloodshed amid much smaller, albeit very regrettable, annual casualties; and the fact that the high incident rate during the bad years was at odds with all that had I been hearing about the rarity of a dangerous encounter.

I had been sent a magazine article that described the work of a young scientist, Vidya Athreya, in Akole, a district 100 miles north-east of Mumbai. In 2003 Akole had begun to suffer an increased incidence of leopard attacks on humans, in a repeat of a pattern that had started a few years earlier in nearby Junnar. In both cases, there had been a rapid increase in the acreage of sugar cane plantations which encroached into forest land and other leopard habitat. Instead of forcing the leopards out, the new, man-made habitat provided plenty of cover and prey: fewer wild boar and deer, but plentiful street dogs and other domestic animals. As livestock losses increased, people with no previous experience of leopards sought to defend their animals, often leading to their own injuries and deaths. So the Forest Department began capturing leopards and removing them to remoter areas with more natural habitat. Almost simultaneously, attacks increased in other areas, too, where there had been no significant habitat change. The Yawal Wildlife Sanctuary covers over 170 sq km in Jalgaon district of Maharashtra. Though the forests of Yawal have a naturally high leopard population and have been dotted with human settlements for a long time, there was no history of conflict. This suddenly changed when six leopard attacks occurred in the last two months of 2003 in villages that had never previously suffered an attack. Vidya's electronic tagging programme enabled her to establish that the culprits were the same animals that only a few months earlier had been captured and removed from Junnar.

The policy of translocating problem leopards to distant habitat had affected SGNP too. Research showed that as well as translocating the problem with the animal, the policy actually exacerbated the conflict. The released animals had no familiarity with the habitat, the prey base, the lie of the land or the existing pattern of leopard territories, into which they had been plunged and left to cope as best they could. Desperate for food, these landless vagrants had no option but to overcome their natural fear of humans.

In light of Vidya's findings, the Forest Department was quick to abandon the well-intended but flawed policy, turning instead to programmes of awareness-raising and conflict management led by people like Krishna. In the sugar-cane growing areas husbandry techniques adapted to afford greater protection from leopards, and in SGNP the situation quickly returned to normal. Since 2007, the annual casualty figures in the *padas* have dropped further, to the odd non-fatal incident or two a year at most.[1]

Gir

There is a *raga* for every part of the day, such as the time when the darkness meets the dawn, a tranquil moment called *Brahmamuhurta*, the Ayurvedic point of maximum stillness of the mind. The music for this time is the *raga* known as Lalit, a serene improvisation on a scale unlike any that would be familiar to western ears.[2] In the Gir Forest, nature's Lalit is a coarse but soothing welcome from the jungle crow, and a seven-note descending-then-rising melody from the Tickell's blue flycatcher, whose plumage is that of the pre-dawn itself: twilight blue and orange.

Manisha Rajput had selected a route that plunged us into the cool green-gold morning of the acacias, where we had the sounds of the forest to ourselves. We took with us only the sometimes purring, sometimes growling voice of our own jeep.

To these the forest added the stabbing notes of red-wattled lapwings whenever we crossed a stream, or the penetrating mewl of peafowl from the denser areas of jungle. We entered a zone dominated by teak trees: denser growth, dimmer colours, and the unique sound of teak leaves in the wind. The size of dinner plates, they were stiff and thick and turning brown and made a gentle, woody clatter as the breeze ran through them, or as they detached themselves and made their swaying descent through the branches to land among the other fallen. On the same breeze came the whiff of kill, of a sambar brought down the day before, and we followed it out of the teak and into the savannah. A whisper from Manisha:

"There's one, and another!" We trained our binoculars on the space between the top of the tall herb-layer of *Senna tora* and the lowest leaves of an acacia. Manisha had spotted two adolescent Asiatic lions about thirty yards away. One stood side-on to us, facing right, head angled slightly upwards at a haughty angle. It seemed to gaze into the distance as it flicked its tail up into a graceful curve like a sideways 'J'. The other was lying down, half asleep and half-hidden. Just discernible through the *Senna* stems was the dark curve of the deer's bloated belly; its smell was only mildly putrescent in the relatively cool air of the morning.

"Lucky you are", whispered Manisha.

We were a few hundred yards farther along the track when two lionesses appeared from the undergrowth behind the jeep walking towards and then past us. The first emerged into the glow of the low sun which rendered her fur the colour of rice straw; a few seconds behind her, the second lioness stayed closer to the shading vegetation, and appeared the colour of dry grass. The lionesses crossed the track about forty yards ahead of us and disappeared into the grass to our right.

We moved on, but stopped again after a short distance. Three young women appeared from around a bend farther along the track, walking towards us. They could have been sisters, two in their late teens, the other perhaps fifteen. The two older girls were dressed in the Maldhari style *kameez*, bright plain-coloured tops with contrasting patterned panels across the bust, and dark-coloured *lungi* – a kind of sarong. As I was later to find was normal, they wore ample jewellery even as they went about everyday tasks: heavy-looking (but hollow) silver anklets, thin chords of leather supporting pendants at the neck, gold studs and pendants adorning their ears. The youngest was in plain *shalwar-kameez*, trousers and shirt, with no jewellery that I could see apart from the leather necklace and pendant, and whereas her companions had their heads covered by the ubiquitous *dupatta* headscarves, her hair was tied back and two loops of plain rope wound round her head like an Arab *agal*.

"Are they going to be ok? They're walking towards the lions, and the lions are walking towards them." I knew the answer, but the question seemed to insist on being asked. Manisha smiled.

"It's their everyday experience. They are coming back from the stream where they wash every morning. You can see they are not nervous or frightened."

Originally the Maldhari were nomads from Sindh and Rajasthan, and other parts of Gujarat. Although they are a recognised tribe, with certain rights enshrined in law, the name Maldhari is an occupational term – keeper (*dhari*) of livestock (*mal*) – that can apply to people from different castes and communities. They live throughout the Gir, in homesteads called *neses*, typically occupied by one large extended family or two or three couples and their children.

Before we headed south out of the city of Rajkot in the north-western state of Gujarat, Manisha had taken me to meet her friend Bhushan Pandya. For nearly thirty years Bhushan would drive a hundred miles to the Gir and spend a day or two each week photographing the forest, its lions and its people, fitting his hobby around the demands of running a colour processing business. He created an invaluable visual archive of the cat that had been hunted to the brink of extinction under British rule, but had clawed its way back, to a carefully-protected population of over 500 today. One night, five years ago, Bhushan lost control of his car during a monsoon downpour. He spent seven months in hospital in Mumbai, his neck broken, but refusing to accept doctors' prognosis that he would never walk again. Eventually, one six-inch step at a time, he walked out of hospital and returned home to Rajkot.

I took an instant liking to Bhushanbhai. No longer able to travel around the forest independently, he exuded an undiminished passion for the Gir and its lions. He was eager to hear about our plans, and to field question after question about lions, people and conservation.

"There is huge public support in Gujarat for wildlife protection," he said. "It's just that at election time only big infrastructure projects get discussed and no-one makes the connection with habitat loss until it's too late."

I was curious to know where this support for wildlife protection came from.

"You've heard of *ahimsa*, I suppose?" I had, and vaguely understood it to mean 'non-violence', associating it with Gandhi's *Satyagraha* civil resistance movement. "It means 'to do no harm'," explained Bhushan, "and it doesn't just apply to people, in fact it mainly applies to animals. Gandhiji was from Gujarat and here *ahimsa* is very strong.

Two weeks before my trip to India, Asiatic lion conservation suffered a devastating blow. On 3 October I received a message from Manisha, who was busy planning my visit.

...Since from 15 days in Gir, suddenly 21 lions died
bcos of some viral diseases so all the scenario has
been changed but will give u update in a day or two...

The following day another message from Manisha confirmed the presence of canine distemper, and the first reports started to appear in the Indian press and from there, the world's media. In total 23 lions died in the outbreak.

Since the 1990s there have been plans to translocate some animals to the Palpur-Kuno Wildlife Sanctuary in northern Madhya Pradesh to reduce the species' vulnerability to epidemic disease. Gujarat state officials resisted the plan, and proponents of the scheme accused Gujarat of placing the Gir's unique status as the home of the Asiatic lion above the needs of the animals themselves. In April 2013, the Indian Supreme Court ordered Gujarat to cooperate. With the election of the former Chief Minister of Gujarat, Narendra Modi, as India's Prime Minister in 2014, the state's policy became national policy, enforced over the Supreme Court's orders through a process of prolonged foot-dragging. Bhushanbhai's view, highly informed, independent of Government, and coming from a passionate advocate for the Gir, was something I needed to tease out before we left the city for the forest.

"There are many areas in southern Saurashtra where lions can make their homes. If corridors are maintained, the lion can spread. Already, there are new populations on the coast, where the Gir population has expanded."

"So you don't see a need to build up a new population outside Gujarat?"

"In theory, it could work but the reality is different. The tribal communities of Madhya Pradesh are not like the Maldhari of Gir. Here lions are used to living alongside humans and vice versa, this is not true in Madhya Pradesh. In a heavily populated country like India, wildlife cannot exist without community support. Scientists don't study that aspect, they worry about habitat, site conservation, ecology."

Across India, dairy herds – buffalos or cows – and millions of street-cows return from their pasturings and wanderings back to their villages, *neses* and city byres during a gentle hour when the dust kicked up by their hooves is tinted by the colours of the setting sun. It is known as cow-dust hour, and there is a *raga* for this time, too: 'Marwa'. Like Lalit, it comprises tones that seem strange to western ears,[3] homeless and wandering. Our plan was to return to the forest in the cool of the evening, to visit Vaniavav, a *nes* that was home to Hardabhai, his son Meraman, Meraman's wife, Janaben, Mahesh, their son, and Mina, Payal and Jalpa, their daughters.

There was a music in the sounds of the sunset chores at Vaniavav, as I watched the buffalo milked and corralled for the night and listened to the ringing sound the metal pails make when the first jets of milk strike. Meraman's tenor voice calling from across the compound, with a questioning inflexion and Janaben's bell-like answering cadence. Grunts and lows from the animals. *Pic! pic!* from red-wattled lapwings. I was standing under an overhanging roof, on a raised verandah, at the edge of a five-foot drop down into the courtyard which was packed with buffalo. Hardabhai, the silver-haired, yellow-moustached, decades-weathered head of the family, joined us and sat opposite Manisha on a cot that rested against the back wall. He was immediately provided with a stainless steel saucer of hot buffalo milk which he balanced by the rim in the raised tips of his left-hand fingers, between two of which was also wedged an inch of roll-up. He looked tough and fit and old and tired at the same time. He was dressed entirely in white *kediyu-chorno*. The *kediyu*, a long-sleeved smock-shirt, pleated at the chest and reaching to the waist, was grimy from the day's sweat and dust. The *chorno*, wide pantaloons tied loosely at the ankles, were a bright, cleaner white somehow.

Janaben finished her duties, and sat on the lip of the verandah, turned half towards us, and half-hidden from my view. Meraman arrived and sat next to his father, and his own son, Mahesh, a boy of about thirteen, sat between them. They all looked at me, finally ready for the interview we had come for, a conversation about an incident two years ago, when Meraman was attacked by a lion and hospitalised.[4]

"Our kids, they are not afraid of lions," Hardabhai began. "The reason the lions don't eat the Maldhari is because they are family to us and we are family to them, they know very well we are family and they cannot eat us."

"We used to have 200 cattle now we have 20-30 cattle of which 4 or 5 are milking cattle and sometimes one is taken by a lion. We don't complain," said Janaben. "Our children don't have the advantages that city children have, so they wherever they go they suffer by comparison and can't get on. We Maldhari are ready to leave the forest, but if we go, the lion will not survive."

"When Meraman was attacked, even the lion crossed a boundary," said Hardabhai. "In the daytime they are not allowed to come near the *nes*, and it had never, ever happened before. It happened because some people from the city disturbed them, for the lion safari. So some of the buffalo and the cattle were drinking water, and the lioness came, and I told Meraman not to go out, but Meraman went out to the corral in his bare feet and stood between the lion and the buffalo calf. That's when the lion attacked, it caught him by the shoulder."

"I tried to punch the lion's nose with my free arm," said Meraman. "Then my father came out and hit her on the head with a stick and between us we saw it off."

"Were you frightened?"

"I didn't have time to think."

"What about afterwards, when you looked back on the incident?"

"Where will I go if I'm frightened? It's our daily life. If a lion catches our buffalo, we have to go to release it."

"He was too badly injured to come home so I sent him to the road, where he could get a lift to Mendarda. A car was going past, so they took him to the doctor," Hardabhai explained.

"I have asked Hardabhai if he would prefer his life without lion," said Manisha.

"No. Every day we have a lion visitor here, every day. We are the people who are providing them food worth 50,000 or one *lakh* [100,000] rupees; no-one else can offer that food to them, so they respect us."

"I don't get that, sorry."

"Because a buffalo costs 50,000 or one *lakh*," Manisha explained.

"When a lion kills our buffalo, we let him finish eating, we don't have negativity. We embrace it.[5] And if people are coming to see lions from around the world, there must be something in the lion, there must be some divine... divine thing in the lion, so we are blessed that we are living with them. Every small living creature has a soul in them. If we are going somewhere in the early morning and we see a lion's face, it is auspicious for us."

"It will be a good day," I suggested.

"It will be a good day," agreed Manisha.

We visited Manisha's friend Devvrat Bhatt, son of the Ahmedabad writer Druv Bhatt, whose novel *Akoopar* is about the life of the Maldhari and the lions of the Gir, the English translation of which Manisha had sent me before my visit. The book features real people barely disguised: I had already met Revtubha Raijana, a retired biology teacher from Keshod who is depicted as 'Ravuba' in the story. When we had called in on him to break the journey from Rajkot, he explained how he had experimented with 'in-nature teaching', conducting classes in the Gir Forest during camping trips from school. The demand for such sessions was such that he founded the Sky Forest Youth Club to encourage young people to stargaze and to watch wildlife.

Devvrat's house is on the edge of Sasan Gir, amid farmland that separates the town from the forest. As we sat in the shade of a mango tree, drinking tea and eating Manisha's home-made *kachori*, and as a booted eagle appeared above our heads, circling a swell of rising air, I told him that reading his father's novel was the perfect preparation for this visit.

"Do you want to have a chat with him?"

"Is he here?"

"No, he's at home in Ahmedabad, but I can call him." Moments later I had Devvrat's mobile phone to my ear, and I was gabbling an explanation for my visit, and for disturbing him at home.

"I don't consider myself an activist," Dhruv explained, "more of an eyewitness. My books have covered all sorts of subjects that interest me, religion, tribes, castes."

"I must say I feel humbled by the Maldhari and their attitude to the lions and to their environment," I said. "There's a kind of harmony...I don't know, some sense that they understand completely where they fit into the forest ecosystem."

"It's why I wanted to write about the Gir," said Dhruv. "We've been coming here with the kids for years. The more I understood the place, the more I realised that we have to be friends with everything – from stones to humans."

"That's almost exactly what Revtubha told me the other day."

"Yes, it's a local saying, in English it's something like 'from stones we have to take care of humankind.'"

TWELVE

Perspective

Reckonings

A few years ago I was half-listening to someone whose name I don't recall being interviewed on the radio. Like me, he started his professional life in 1983, and like me, he was contemplating his forthcoming retirement. His work was in supporting people with severe mental disorders, a profession I had once seriously considered joining. Through a link between my school and a local club for young people with learning disabilities, I spent one evening a week enjoying my first experience of voluntary work. During my university years in the late 1970s conservation jobs were relatively few, and I had half-decided to train for such a career. The man on the radio was commenting on the state of his profession and of the nation's attitude to mental health 35 years on. There is a long way to go, he said, but at least things aren't as bad as when he started in 1983. I thought of all the cause-led careers I might have pursued, and for many the assessment would be identical, from cancer research to child welfare: we have a long way to go, but we have come a long way, too. How would a similar stock-take look for my own world of wildlife conservation?

In 1983 red kites did not fly in Yorkshire, nor over any of the roughly 25 English, Scottish and Northern Irish counties in which they breed today. White-tailed eagles were long lost and attempts to bring them back had failed. Corncrakes were more common and widespread than now, but in the late stages of a seemingly terminal decline. Badgers were rarely encountered after decades of persecution but were showing signs of recovery; the otter's status remained parlous. This was what I had entered conservation for – to prevent the most threatened species from becoming lost from Britain, or extinct worldwide. By 1983 avocets and ospreys, two species that had talismanic status – the hope-charms and logos of the movement – were steadily re-establishing themselves, and a sense was emerging that loss was reversible.

With one possible exception, it is highly unlikely that any of these cases of recovery would have happened if left to public authorities alone; they all needed sustained commitment, determination in the face of set-backs, and considerable investment, all of which would have melted away over the timescales involved without conservation organisations to provide the necessary stamina. The exception is the otter, which eventually was to benefit from a concerted clean-up and restoration of the riparian environment led in large part by government agencies.

"To renew the living fabric of the land so that it also replenishes the spirits of its human inhabitants seems to me as close as one can come to a single expression of the aims of a total conservation policy."[1] I first read those words, written by Richard Mabey in the early 1980s, when I had begun to believe that a career in conservation might be possible. More and more jobs were being advertised as charities, local authorities and the Nature Conservancy Council saw a gradual growth in need, opportunity and funds. But I had left university without sitting for my degree, grabbing instead a work opportunity at the bottom rung of the industrial management ladder. I don't know what I was thinking, but there was a new book out – Mabey's *The Common Ground* – that I could mine for some extra learning and ideas to take into an interview, should one be offered.

It is strange to re-read *The Common Ground* after forty years. It is simultaneously out-of-date as to the details, and utterly contemporary as to the underlying concerns. At Mabey's time of writing (1979), controversy was raging over the government's plan to cull grey seals in Scotland, which had been suspended pending further studies. Commercial fishermen were complaining that the seals, whose Scottish population had been growing and now made up half the world's total, were depleting fish stocks. The government accepted their view without serious challenge and agreed to a six-year population reduction programme. Scientists and conservationists rallied to argue that the evidence to support such a plan was non-existent, and that the grey seals were being used as a scapegoat for bad fisheries management. The beleaguered Prime Minister, James Callaghan, had come into office unelected following Harold Wilson's sudden resignation, and was struggling to hold his government together. 15,000 letters of protest at the cull were to convince him that this was a controversy he could do without. For 1979, read 2019; for fisheries, read livestock; for grey seal, read badger. The respective public outcries had played out through radically different media. Otherwise, the main difference was the speed of response by the governments of the day, in turn a function of their hold on power. Until recently there was little sign that years of outrage at the badger cull, and all the wattage of amplification provided by social media, was hitting home. Successive governments had been buying time until veterinary developments could provide a pathway out of political stalemate.

One of *The Common Ground*'s biggest surprises is the simple fact of its existence. It was instigated by the Nature Conservancy Council so that people should know more about conservation "warts and all", to quote its Chairman Professor Sir Fred Holliday's foreword. NCC was looking to engender a public debate on issues that, despite their self-evident public interest, had too often been tackled using opaque processes behind the scenes. Mabey was given complete freedom to express his findings as he saw fit, and free access to internal documents and to NCC staff; and encouraged to speak to as many people outside the organisation as he wished. Such confidence on the part of a statutory conservation body would be unimaginable today; and was probably mis-placed then. Ten years later, Holliday resigned when the Thatcher government broke up the NCC[2] with no prior consultation. Government responsibilities for nature conservation were devolved to the separate UK countries, a full nine years before Tony Blair's Labour government set up the new Scottish, Welsh and Northern Irish administrations. The Conservative Party was no fan of devolution, but Environment Minister Nicholas Ridley, whose family interests included landowning and property development in environmentally sensitive areas, was determined to emasculate what he saw as an overly powerful threat to property rights and the economy.

That act was a sign of how far the conservation community had come in the decade since Mabey's survey. In 1979 there were still many in the profession who had fought for their country and were determined to play their part in the nation's rebuilding. None was prepared for the pastoral meltdown that began at the same time. The 1960s and 70s saw some of the first set-piece conservation cases to arise under the post-war site-based conservation legislation, in which an earnest scientific community went into battle hopelessly outgunned by the industrial giants of the day. In 1966 ICI, whose full name – Imperial Chemical Industries – is Linnaean in its succinct encapsulation of the nature of the beast, chose the botanically and geologically unique Upper Teesdale as the site for a new water supply reservoir serving industrial plant 54 miles away on Teesside. In what was at the time an unusual move, Parliament set up a Select Committee to hear evidence from both sides of the debate. ICI fielded barristers whose entire professional lives were spent in such a milieu. Facing them were scientists whose passion for the genetics of the Teesdale violet or the metamorphosis of dolerite rock into sugar limestone was made to seem exclusive and narrow-minded against future-facing rhetoric championing jobs and technology. They stood no chance, and were not helped by the legislation on which they believed their arguments were founded. For all the multiplicity of conservation designations available today, it was and remains the case that they are legally underpinned or undermined according to whether or not they are Sites of Special Scientific Interest.

Richard Mabey has consistently pioneered new ways of thinking about landscape, nature, place, culture and the labyrinth of interconnections between them. *The Common Ground* recognised the need to raise the standards of technical expertise, analytical rigour and public relations artistry brought to bear on issues of the day. At the same time, it reads like a prescient warning and a plea: not to rely so heavily on them that we ignore the human dimension on which long-term success depends. His entreaty *to renew the living fabric of the land so that it also replenishes the spirits of its human inhabitants* will have seemed old-fashioned and romantic to many in 1980. On the other hand, it could have been written yesterday.

The Wasted Land

The Common Ground has been updated – in effect – by Mark Cocker's *Our Place*. Together, they remind us that failure to treat land systemically is not new. Over nearly a thousand years – since 1066 in fact – land-based prerogatives have relentlessly narrowed in scope until barely any of the private privileges of land ownership are subordinate to any of the shared benefits of good land management. From the enclosures of the seventeenth to nineteenth centuries onwards, land has become consecrated to the greater profit and pleasure of the landlords, always supported by a vested and self-serving body politic. Gone are the common lands that yielded hay, pasture, watering, brash and turf, space and air. Gone, the copses that provided industrial raw materials, forage, pannage and underwood for the peasantry. Gone, the extensive saltmarshes that buffered the coast and sheltered natural fish nurseries: reclaimed, ploughed, seeded and sprayed to make more unitary purpose farmland.

With the advent in the mid-twentieth century of centralised policy interventions by government – and soon after, by the EU[3] – came a real opportunity to reverse some of the widely-acknowledged injustices of these historic trends. However, throughout the developed world, and nowhere more so than in the UK, wherever governments intervened, it was with the avowed intention of speeding up those very processes. The beneficiaries were always the landowners who already operated at scale; the losers, always the small farmers and the wider workforce. As I set out earlier, and as is plain to see for anyone with any interest in nature, the quality of the farmed environment, measured by the richness and abundance of wildlife, went into freefall and has not stopped falling.

Millions of words have been penned by scientists, civil servants, political advisers, advocates, policy-makers, journalists, economists and radio soap scriptwriters on the environmental impact of Europe's Common Agricultural Policy. Millions more on its impact on income inequality, small farm businesses, markets, trade and land prices. By 2013 the direct cost to European tax-payers had risen to €58 bn, most of it destined to be recycled around the largest farmers and agri-industries of the inner club of longer-standing EU countries. Despite percentage budget reductions in recent years, the CAP remains the biggest intervention in public policy in the world, and by far the most Gargantuan example of disjunct policy-making in history. In 2016, days after the UK voted narrowly to leave the European Union, I penned the final words of my book *The Long Spring*. The desolation that the referendum result had left me feeling was slightly tempered by the thin hope that...

...the UK now has an opportunity to support
land free of the arbitrary restrictions, idiocies and
injustices of the Common Agricultural Policy. Rather
than obscuring, institutionalising and rewarding bad
land management, post-Brexit subsidies must invest
in land as a national asset, invite and embrace public
scrutiny, and be held to account. Food production,
wood production, water, carbon and wildlife can be
re-amalgamated and supported in a more integrated
way: the key is not to concern ourselves with
attaching administrative labels to land and the people
who occupy it. The agriculturally unproductive and
dysfunctional uplands, and especially the National
Parks, along with floodplains and coastal areas
fighting hopeless battles with the sea, are obvious
places to experiment with new models. If the UK
can develop a subsidy system that is economically,
politically and environmentally sustainable it could
even be a basis for the eventual replacement of the
CAP, and therefore the reconnection of people and
nature, across the EU and beyond.

The CAP is a classic case of a linear, non-systemic policy: it set out to solve a single problem – the need to secure food supply[4] – and created many more. Most notorious was the rampant over-production that reached a scandalous peak in 2006, when the EU had stockpiled 13,476,812 tonnes of cereal, rice, sugar and milk products and 3,529,002 hectolitres of alcohol, in order to maintain guaranteed prices for the farmer. Releasing this hoard into world markets at bargain basement prices ruined third world farmers whose own produce suddenly seemed expensive in comparison. An unspoken impact – later to be avowed as policy – was the acceleration of a process that had begun decades before: the swallowing of small farms by large ones, leading to hundreds of thousands of small and medium-sized farm businesses closing. Another effect was a plunge in Europe's bird populations, which was merely the most visible sign of a wholesale collapse in the diversity of wildlife in the farmed landscape. This was in turn the harbinger of a comprehensive environmental calamity: agriculture contributes 10 percent of Europe's greenhouse gas emissions while nitrate pollution has washed into Europe's seas, creating toxic algal blooms that in places have eliminated coastal biodiversity and caused livestock and even human fatalities.[5,6]

Had the CAP started life as a land optimisation programme, and had post-war food security, rural development, environmental safeguarding and the husbanding of natural resources been its complimentary aims, none of this would have happened. The programme that probably would not have been called the Common Agricultural Policy would have been capable, through some small adjustment, of incorporating net carbon sequestering to its suite of purposes as soon as its planet-saving criticality was first recognised. Successive 'reforms' in 1992, 1999, 2003, 2009 and 2013 addressed the problems of high spending and over-production by directing some money away from supporting commodity prices and towards rural development and agri-environment schemes. They also made a complex behemoth of a system more complex still, and even less transparent.

Direct payments – paying farmers for owning farmland – still accounts for 72% of CAP spending. Of this, 80% of the money goes to the biggest 20% of recipients, and 30% to the biggest two percent.[7] Small-scale fraud occurs everywhere, while in Italy the CAP has long been absorbed into the Mafia business model. Repeated failure by EU officials and politicians to allow open scrutiny as to where this massive public spending ends up has left it to journalists to uncover, one of whom, Ján Kuciak, paid with his life. Kuciak and his fiancée Martina Kušnírová were murdered in February 2018 while investigating Calabrian 'Ndragheta mobsters who had built relationships with powerful politicians and infiltrated the Slovakian farm industry in order to reap the subsidies. Their deaths were a catalyst around which anti-corruption sentiment crystallised, and the government fell in elections held on 29 February 2020. Slovakia is not alone among the new EU countries of Central and Eastern Europe where populist demagogue leaders have been cashing in. In December 2019 the European Commission found the Czech Prime Minister Andrej Babiš to be in conflict of interest. As the owner of an agri-business empire he had received millions of Euros a year – $42 million in 2018 alone according to a *New York Times* investigation[8] – under the CAP subsidy regime that he and his fellow EU leaders were responsible for. In Hungary, Viktor Orban's government has auctioned off thousands of acres of state land to his family members and close associates, who as a result qualify for millions in CAP subsidies.

The RSPB, the National Trust and the county Wildlife Trusts collectively own and manage hundreds of thousands of acres of qualifying land and EU agri-environment payments have become a valuable source of conservation funding. Such schemes work best when they are deployed by conservationists in conservation-focussed farmland; or on family farms where the owners' personal passions may lead them to choose the less profitable option. As Director of the RSPB's operations in northern England, I set up a farm business advice unit of ecologically-trained agronomists and agriculturally-literate ecologists to do what commercial and government advisers were reluctant to do – ensure that some of the new 'reform' payments were directed at real conservation priorities and achieved real conservation benefit. In the uplands especially, we found a farming community highly receptive to our ideas, as long as we did the paperwork and agreed with them what they needed to do, where and when. Birds that had been clinging on in the traditionally-managed marginal lands included the twite, an upland finch dependent on seed-rich hay meadows, and the lapwing, in rapid decline due to the chaotic pattern of under-grazing, over-grazing and drainage that had been leaching the life from the uplands, acre by acre, for decades.

Yet agri-environment payments remain calibrated to ensure that pro-conservation farming cannot be more financially attractive than intensive food production. At worst, farmers can still be paid for environmental options that interfere little with their operations, have little overall impact on a business plan built on intensive farming and generous acreage subsidies, and have no discernible bearing on the trajectory of wildlife decline. The EU's own Court of Auditors concluded, in December 2017, that CAP greening was "unlikely to provide significant benefits for the environment and climate" because it changed practices on just 5% of EU farmland.[9]

As the European Union embarks on its latest round of 'reforms', without the net financial contribution provided by the UK; and as the UK introduces its own replacement system, the case for fundamental change has never been stronger. In January 2020, the UK's final month of EU membership, the government presented its Agriculture Bill to Parliament. (For clarity: this is a Bill concerning England's agriculture, the four countries of the UK having devolved responsibility for farming policy.) Conservation organisations have taken encouragement from DEFRA's repeated commitment that from now on public money will only be paid to farmers who deliver public goods. The National Farmers' Union's carefully-worded response lauded what its President, Minette Batters, saw as confirmation that "the Agriculture Bill now recognises that food production and caring for the environment go hand-in-hand." The farming lobby's task is two-fold: to keep food production (and by implication subsidies for food production) coupled in the minds of policy-makers with environmental protection; and to play down agriculture's environmental cost.

Brexit has therefore delivered the NFU a public relations gift. It comes in the form of the very real and unpalatable prospect of trade negotiations leading to the UK having to accept cheap imports of low-quality food produced to low animal welfare, food safety and environmental standards. The NFU has been quick to link all these issues and treat them as one. In comparison to the US and much of the world the UK may maintain relatively high standards of animal welfare and food safety, and it would be self-evidently wrong if we were to import food that would be illegal to produce in the UK. Whether the new Agriculture Bill will enable farmers to be subsidised simply for not breaking legal standards is – at the time of writing – unclear. It would be like paying drivers not to exceed the speed limit in order to improve public safety. Recognising this, the NFU keeps environmental stewardship (for which the case for public subsidy is strong) and animal welfare (for which the subsidy case is weak) closely linked, implying that existing standards are high in both. Minette Batters's speech went on to say that "farmers are rightly proud of their environmental efforts and it is crucial this new policy recognises and rewards the environmental benefits they deliver, both now and in the future," before delivering her bottom-line demand. "The government's commitment to invest in supporting farmers to improve productivity will be critical, given the delivery of sustainable and climate-friendly food systems cannot be achieved in the absence of viable and profitable farm businesses."

The farming industry and conservation share one overwhelming concern, that post-Brexit trade deals and budgetary freedom do not lead to a race to the bottom on standards. On 24 January the NFU arranged for a letter, signed by Minette Batters for the NFU, Beccy Speight, the RSPB's Chief Executive, and 60 other signatories from farming and environmental organisations, to be sent to Boris Johnson. They wrote:

> While the liberalisation of global trade in recent decades has been successful in growing economies, providing jobs and lowering prices for consumers, it has failed to deal with the negative impacts of such growth – most evident today in the challenges of climate change, loss of biodiversity and concerns over the welfare of the farm animals we rear. Brexit means the UK can show leadership in pioneering a new type of global trading system; one that moves away from the narrow and dated focus on ever cheaper goods, regardless of how they are produced, to one that rises to the challenges of climate change and promotes more sustainable models of production and consumption across the world.

The two sectors have circled nervously in each other's orbits for decades, and both sense that the stakes are higher than ever. The letter makes clear that "there may be differences of opinion as to the best way of achieving" the outcomes they advocate. As the details of the new policy take shape, so those differences will emerge into the open: both sides are taking risks. Farming organisations who were among the architects of protectionist policies are seeking to position themselves in the vanguard of a transition to a new reality; one that will remain benign and lucrative for the biggest producers. Conservation organisations are banking on the public goods principle being both well-funded and properly directed at biodiversity and climate change outcomes. If comfort is sought in current government rhetoric, conservationists will be quietly confident. If it is based on historic precedent and on policy-makers' innate conservatism, it is the NFU who will be buoyed.

A good sign is the label given to one of the schemes likely to attract a significant proportion of the £3 billion currently spent each year on funding the UK's share of the CAP. DEFRA says its plans for a new Environmental Land Management Scheme or ELMS, will provide an income stream for farmers and land managers who protect and preserve the natural environment, and find ways of integrating this into their food, timber and other commercial activities. Sceptics question whether DEFRA will ensure that payments reward good practice rather than simply paying less responsible farmers not to pollute. Worse still would be to fudge the criteria for payments to such an extent that they worsen the situation they are intended to solve. For example, carbon sequestration payments, if used for planting trees in peatlands, would be likely to release more greenhouse gases than would ever be sequestered by the trees.

The National Audit Office notes that rural development programmes under the CAP have been consistently undersubscribed in England and that DEFRA has not yet demonstrated that it can achieve its ambitions for ELMS. It is noteworthy, therefore, that a late addition in the drafting of the Agriculture Bill was the stipulation that the government will "take regard to the need to encourage the production of food by producers in England." The NFU calls this a "robust starting point" for designing the new support programmes. Others fear that it is an early sign of backsliding toward payments designed to boost private profit rather than support environmental progress.

The biggest risk that conservationists are taking is to appear to benchmark their ambitions against EU agri-environment schemes that show little sign of restoring farmland biodiversity. Payments fall far short of the reparations needed after 58 years of the CAP. ELMS and the principle of public money for public goods must be applied boldly to the monumental challenge of halting wildlife's decline and creating a springboard for rebuilding it. Isolated instances of success – shrill carder bees here and corncrakes there – are good news in themselves, but risk masking the failure of the agri-environment concept as currently practiced.

Loss revisited

In the past three decades, species-focussed conservation has diverged along two distinct paths. The first is the path of restoration: the reintroduction of lost species or the rebuilding of critical populations and their habitats. Reintroduction proposals are ever more audacious and controversial, as excitement and fear about the potential return of beavers, lynx and wolves captures the headlines and the imagination. Targeted measures to bring surviving but rare species back from the brink are informed by decades of science, trial and error and a collective experience amounting to thousands of person-years in the UK alone. Hope resides in these sometimes spectacularly successful showcases of the art of the possible. The underlying condition, however, is of a Great Thinning, to use Michael McCarthy's stark term for the dramatic fall in the abundance and diversity of wildlife in the UK and across the world. This requires a different path, a poorly-charted one that winds steeply uphill.

As the then Environment Correspondent for the *Independent* newspaper, McCarthy first wrote about the vanishing of abundance in 2010, and the response from older readers in particular was intense. Two years later he requested readers share their specific memories, and there was an intense response once more:

> People over 50 remember enormous flocks of
> lapwings over farmland, and corn buntings on every
> telegraph wire, and vast clouds of starlings wheeling
> against the evening sky; they remember nettle beds
> full of small tortoiseshell caterpillars, roadside verges
> full of flowers, gardens full of songbirds and ditches
> full of frogs and toads – all gone. The most common
> image is of the car windscreen, splattered with moths
> and other insects at the end of every night-time
> journey in summer. Now the windscreens are clean.[10]

A one-time schoolboy moth enthusiast himself, McCarthy's own response was to write *The Moth Snowstorm: nature and joy*[11] a heartfelt and moving classic of conservation writing. As I described earlier,[12] great is the challenge to make wide swathes of countryside hospitable once more to the plants, insects and birds that are supposed to be widespread, common species of everyday experience, but whose decline has been steady and inexorable. The human co-victims – those whose response to nature's impoverishment is visceral, emotional and perhaps even clinical – feel this denaturing more directly than any national or global extinction of species they may never have encountered in person.

Across the country small groups are popping up to rebuild nature field by field, street by street, running backwards the process by which nature has been disappearing from their lives. In his book *Our Place* my friend Mark Cocker sees the plethora of new local conservation groups as a sign that mainstream conservation charities appear increasingly irrelevant to ordinary people who want to be more emotionally identified with action on the ground. Charities such as the National Trust and the RSPB are "trapped by the size of their membership", which makes them cautious, he says. Viewing it from the inside, I might express it somewhat differently.

As recently as the 1970s the concept of a global common weal to which local action contributed was a very restricted one. We believed in a vague idea that the wildlife of the Amazon belonged to us all, as did the ocean-going whales; or that the world's forests and oceans influenced its weather. *Think global, act local* is a mantra coined in that era[13] to encapsulate a philosophy conceived in 1915 by Scots town planner and pioneering environmentalist Sir Patrick Geddes. Geddes thought of the city as a series of common interlocking patterns, "an inseparably interwoven structure", akin to a flower. It was a conscious reference to the iconography of Eastern philosophy, which he believed more readily understood the interconnectedness of life as a whole. Geddes was therefore an early advocate and practitioner of systems thinking and its application to the human environment, 67 years before Capra. A century later, his thinking seems as far from the mainstream as ever.

In 2017 work began on HS2, a 345-mile high-speed rail line linking London and Birmingham and on to Manchester and

Leeds. Initially costed at £32.7 billion, the budget was revised to £55.6 bn in 2015. Four years later the chair of Europe's largest infrastructure project acknowledged the cost had risen to £88 bn. As the costs spiralled, business leaders, politicians and economists argued first over finely-wrought cost-benefit ratios. When the costings reached levels that bore no relation to the original claims the arguments became more evangelistic, with proponents speaking of their 'beliefs' that the benefits had been undervalued and would far outweigh the up-front costs.

In January 2020 two reports delved further into the cost of HS2. One was commissioned by the new Boris Johnson government and estimated the figure at up to £106 billion.[14] The other found that the full cost to society will include three Special Areas of Conservation, the highest level of protection afforded by the EU law that – at the time of writing – still applies; two Ramsar sites – a measure of quality and global importance for wetlands – and 31 Sites of Special Scientific Interest. The local toll will be staggering: twenty Local Nature Reserves and 693 designated local wildlife sites with a total area of almost 24,000 acres.[15]

The line will also fragment larger tracts of landscape that have been designed and managed as spaces where communities, businesses, schools, families and wildlife can coexist in what Geddes might have recognised as 'inseparably interwoven structures'. These four Nature Improvement Areas and 22 Living Landscapes[16] are local community initiatives, many supported by the larger conservation organisations. Sir John Lawton – a latter-day Patrick Geddes for the natural environment – consciously or otherwise took the 'think global, act local' message and interpreted it for wildlife and people. His ground-breaking report of 2010, *Making Space for Nature*,[17] coined a new mantra in respect of areas managed for wildlife: *more, bigger, better, more joined up*; and it was one whose practical application was clearly understood. His report was commissioned by the government of the day and successive governments have declared themselves committed to both the theory and the practice. HS2, however, has exposed the limits to that commitment. After months of indecision, the Cabinet announced the go-ahead for HS2 on 11 February 2020.

Rarely does the conservation movement face a threat that is as equally troubling for both local and national interests as HS2. Typically, purely local battles are left to local people to fight; they may ask for the support of larger organisations and come away disappointed, perhaps not comprehending the apparent impossibility of fighting for every square inch of green space from a national platform. In the most important national battles, the RSPB and other large organisations often work closely with the local communities who are better able to represent the direct impact on everyday life of a damaging project. The successful fight against Boris Johnson's plans, as Mayor of London, to build a new airport serving London from a man-made island in the spectacularly bird-rich Thames estuary relied equally on the power of local voices and the international perspective and legal expertise of the RSPB. In March 2020 broadcaster and campaigner Chris Packham sought an injunction against so-called enabling works that were well under way along the HS2 route, including tree removal in five ancient woods in Warwickshire and Staffordshire. The RSPB called for a halt to any works during the bird breeding season, while local people exposed HS2 contractors who were using the Covid-19 crisis as cover to speed up the tree-felling without scrutiny. The government's one-time environmental watchdog, Natural England, seemed to be snoozing in its kennel.

In the introductory chapter to this book I wrote that we are becoming desensitised to the loss of nature. The point of global extinction – or of local extirpation – of a species is almost invariably the denouement of a long process of decline over which there is less a grieving, more a resigned acceptance. Can we not at least rage against the dying of the light?

The challenge for the conservation movement is to create in society a sense of urgency and crisis about something as insidious as the Great Thinning. In *The Great Derangement* Amitav Ghosh makes the same point in relation to climate change:

> Consider, for example, the stories that congeal around questions like "Where were you when the Berlin Wall fell?" or "Where were you on 9/11?" Will it ever be possible to ask, in the same vein, "Where were you at 400 ppm?"[18] or "Where were you when the Larsen B ice shelf broke up?"

"Or," the wildlife conservationist might add, "when the last northern white rhino died?" Or the last West African black rhino, Christmas Island pipistrelle, Yangtze river dolphin, slender-billed curlew, Jerdon's courser, all of which appear to have gone extinct since 2004. Perhaps a few will remember Lonesome George, the last Pinta tortoise, a 102-year old resident of the Galápagos Islands, who died on 24 June 2012.

We can never know when we have heard the last cuckoo to sing in our neighbourhood, because our capacity for hope forces us to turn the nub of the question from *when* to *if*. Our hunger for comfort tells us to seek it in the belief that there may be another cuckoo in the next valley, not too far out of earshot. We must never forget that all extinctions start with the first local loss; and that the moment of global extinction is also local, somewhere.

So to return to the claim I made at that conference in York: that loss is built-in to our conservation model. What is conservation getting wrong?

In September 2019 the Luc Hoffmann Institute, a research body set up by the Worldwide Fund for Nature, convened a meeting in Vienna, attended by 70 academics, professionals and researchers to answer that question. Top of the list of reasons why conservation was failing were neo-liberal policies that encourage the over-consumption of resources; the financial starvation by governments of their conservation agencies; subsidies for energy industries, and free rein for agriculture and mining to expand into even the remotest places.

The timing of the meeting for late 2019 was not random. In 2002 the world's governments, as signatories to the Convention on Biological Diversity, had set out to *achieve by 2010 a significant reduction of the current rate of biodiversity loss at the global, regional and national level as a contribution to poverty alleviation and to the benefit of all life on earth.* The year before, the EU Heads of State had decided on an even greater ambition: that *biodiversity decline should be halted with the aim of reaching this objective by 2010.* Of course, neither aim was realised, and at the 2010 Conference of the Parties to the convention, a new strategy for 2011–2020 was adopted. More sophisticated, more detailed, and more focussed on specific goals, it did away with the one-line proclamation of some grandiose aim. Instead, the Parties adopted twenty targets (the so-called Aichi Targets, after the Japanese prefecture in which they were drawn up) which were to contribute to five strategic goals. The goals were to address the causes of biodiversity loss, to reduce pressure on biodiversity, to improve the status of biodiversity, enhance the benefits to all of biodiversity, and to enhance implementation through participation. When the goals are broken down into the twenty targets, the nature of the ambition becomes clear. They all begin with the words "By 2020 ..." and include:[19]

...incentives, including subsidies, harmful to biodiversity are eliminated, phased out or reformed in order to minimize or avoid negative impacts (target 3)

...the rate of loss of all natural habitats, including forests, is at least halved and where feasible brought close to zero (target 5)

...all fish and invertebrate stocks and aquatic plants are managed and harvested sustainably, legally and applying ecosystem-based approaches, so that overfishing is avoided (target 6)

...areas under agriculture, aquaculture and forestry are managed sustainably, ensuring conservation of biodiversity (target 7)

...the extinction of known threatened species has been prevented and their conservation status, particularly of those most in decline, has been improved and sustained (target 12)

The pattern is a familiar one: in 2001, the EU gives itself nine years to achieve a goal so audacious as to be achievable only through revolutionary reform of its most cherished tenets. A year later the rest of the world – led by the capitalist west – decides to face down the forces of global capital in the interests of the home planet and its poor. They fail, and reset the clock, adding another ten years to the timescale – to 2020 – and fail again.

These failures were not close calls, just falling short, but comprehensive, outright, abject debacles. I have done my fair share of time in such intergovernmental conferences. To this day I cannot decide how many among the NGO lobbyists, the civil servants, the politicians and the lawyers were true believers; how many were silent sceptics playing along; who was lying through their teeth as they signed up to commitments they had no intention of fulfilling. Nor can I decide whether it is better to set big targets and fail, or to commit to little at all and claim some small achievement as success. Another conference was due to take place in Kunming, China in October 2020, but was postponed in the wake of the Covid-19 crisis. Meanwhile, a preliminary draft strategy has been prepared. This includes a 2050 vision, five overarching goals for 2030 and for 2050, and 20 action targets for 2030. Serial political failure is the surest symptom of cultural indifference to biodiversity loss; early signs suggest that a further decade of miserable performance is already being pre-empted with a ready-made new set of goalposts.

It would be disastrous if the UK failed to take the opportunity of Brexit to establish bold new nature conservation ambitions. The early signs are encouraging, if for encouragement we look to words, rather than past deeds. We would need to put behind us the fact that the UK has been part of the EU political leadership that gave lip service to the worldwide goal of addressing the decline of biodiversity by 2020, in full knowledge that their policies would have the opposite effect. We would also need to ignore the fact that the UK government was in the vanguard of countries pushing to weaken EU wildlife laws as recently as 2015.[20] The one consistently hopeful trope in this country's within-EU advocacy has been the need to overhaul the CAP and its no-strings largesse. This is now to be tested in a once in a lifetime opportunity for real reform.

As for the perpetual conflict between narrowly-based development and place-based conservation we would have to put our faith in post-Brexit policies that sound idealistic but are ill-defined at best, designed for loss at worst. They include Net Gain, the idea that if a site of conservation value risks being damaged by a development proposal, the developers must not only create compensatory habitat, but include additional acreage so that overall, nature will be rebuilt as development proceeds. The Government's policy statement issued in summer 2019 set out how the forthcoming Environment Bill will approach this issue:

> We are committed to sustainable development
> across our country and delivering much-needed
> housing does not have to come at the expense of
> vital biodiversity. Through the Bill, we will introduce
> a mandatory approach to biodiversity net gain. This
> will require developers to ensure habitats for wildlife
> are enhanced, with a 10% increase in habitat value for
> wildlife compared with the pre-development baseline.
> Exemptions for certain types of development will
> be made in a targeted way, and we will continue to
> work to establish potential approaches to achieving
> biodiversity net gains for nationally significant
> infrastructure projects and marine development,
> which remain out of scope of biodiversity net gain in
> the Bill.

Which, of course, poses more questions than it answers, at least until the Bill passes through Parliament. Parliamentary scrutiny will enable MPs and lobbyists of all persuasions to examine forensically the implications and possible workings of the Net Gain concept. If applied retrospectively to Lodge Hill,[21] it might have given Medway Council and the Ministry of Defence a balanced way of evaluating the true cost to society of their original housing proposals. An obligation to create habitat for 94 pairs of nightingales to replace the 85 pairs whose habitat is under threat would have seen the project shelved years ago on cost and feasibility grounds. Land purchase would add about £17 million to the bill, a relatively small additional sum. Creating perfect nightingale habitat would take many years of high-cost capital works and a commitment to manage the land into the future. House-building on Lodge Hill would not be able to proceed until the nightingale population had at least begun to expand into the new area. It would be simpler to build the houses where the compensatory habitat would have been created.

If this makes Net Gain sound like a fairy story, it is because it requires a wholesale suspension of disbelief. The first assumption is that Net Gain will see biodiversity replaced like-for-like; the second, that creating habitat of the required type and quality is an exact enough science for the results to be guaranteed. Local people will want to insist on the compensation happening close to where the damage is done, while developers will want to push for as much flexibility over location, scale and final results as possible. One assumes that the compensation should be taking effect by the time the damage begins, which may entail waiting five, ten or twenty years before the first sod is lifted. Can ancient woodland be replaced by *future* ancient woodland? Not if unique assemblages of soil microorganisms and the flora associated with them, saproxylic invertebrates and perhaps 2000 species of butterflies, moths, ants, beetles and other insects matter.

You would have to believe that the preventative principle will be strictly applied – that is, that the development proposal would only go forward if there were genuinely no other realistic option, and no alternative, less damaging location. Without this principle, Net Gain becomes a licence to develop anywhere; with this principle applied Lodge Hill would never have been on the table anyway.

Even without the spectre of "exemptions for certain types of development" and the decidedly weasely promise to "work to establish potential approaches" for projects such as HS2, Net

Gain looks like an officially-sanctioned recipe for net loss. Or is my suspension of disbelief around the critical assumptions I've outlined unwarranted? Even if so, there is always HS2, and any other "London-centric vanity project", to quote my friend Steve Ely again[22] (or, indeed, any large-scale infrastructure project that, unlike HS2, proves to be both in the overwhelming national interest and capable of being delivered cost-effectively). For such projects, net loss is implicitly – and nigh-on explicitly – built into the government's Net Gain concept. Why? Because they are *always* conceived as solutions to narrowly-defined problems and *never* conceived systemically. Or, as I preferably expressed it in *The Long Spring:*

Public policy lacks any sense of place.

In public policy wildlife is divorced from its natural setting and the natural setting is divorced from its human context. A site may indeed be of special scientific interest, but to rely on a 70 year old concept to capture the essence of its true value and meaning is to lose the very point of Place.

Value

What does it mean to reorient conservation in order to understand its challenges as a cultural concern, and to find the cultural levers that will enable us to respond? I don't claim to have the answer, but I am sure it starts with a robust assertion of the values that underpin success, and an equally clear rejection of those that undermine it. This book has focussed on the country I know best, where most of my work has been carried out: The United Kingdom. As I stated earlier, we come 29th out of 218 in the league table of countries with the least intact biodiversity, providing a vision of the future for 189 other countries if global wildlife continues its current trajectory. Some of those countries may be better equipped to avert similar levels of loss, because their less anthropocentric cultures would regard it as anathema. I am excited by developments in a few countries in which the fundamental rights of nature are not just being asserted by activists, but enshrined in laws and constitutions. This is perhaps the least 'western' notion possible, one that comes close to abolishing the distinction between humanity and nature.

The Rights of Nature concept acknowledges that nature and all its life forms have the right to exist, persist, maintain and regenerate their vital cycles. And we – the people – have the legal authority and responsibility to enforce these rights on behalf of ecosystems. Ecuador has embodied in its constitution the assertion that nature has inalienable rights, as humans do, and its environmental protection laws and systems now spring from this premise. In Bolivia the Law of the Rights of Mother Earth (*Ley de Derechos de la Madre Tierra*) declares both Earth and its life-systems – which combine human communities and ecosystems – as titleholders of inherent rights specified in the law. The office of the *Defensoría de la Madre Tierra* – a counterpart to the human rights ombudsman or *Defensoría del Pueblo* – is established to act on behalf of nature. In India in 2017, the revered Ganges river and its tributary the Yamuna were briefly accorded the same legal standing. The decision, prompted by religious activism and environmental concern, meant that polluting or damaging the rivers would be legally equivalent to harming a person, and legal custodians were appointed. However, the ruling of the Uttarakhand High Court was almost immediately stayed in the Indian Supreme Court owing to the considerable administrative and legal quandaries that would ensue. In New Zealand the Whanganui river is now recognised as a legal personality, bringing to an end a 140-year dispute and protracted negotiations over Māori land claims. The Uttarakhand ruling was directly modelled on the Whanganui case, and both spring from the premise that the deep cultural connectivity between people and nature is an expression of the very concept of nature itself.

If I think again about the list of hopes that I set out on page 221 and re-express them as cultural shifts, they might go something like this:

We have to stem and reverse the loss of Britain's and the world's natural wealth and beauty. This is agreed by the governments of the world, and it is past time to call them to account, to measure all interventions – policy and practice – according to whether they work to rebuild nature or simply to slow down the rate of its loss. Conservationists need to stop pretending to ourselves that the measures we have fought hard to bring about are yet fit for that purpose. Opportunities to rethink loss and the effect our meek acceptance of it will have on humanity will be rare. If Brexit and Covid don't embolden the conservation sector to promote and achieve bold and radical change, we will have to count it as a fail.

We have to see the goals of tolerance and coexistence between our species and others as fundamental values underpinning the search for solutions when that relationship becomes strained. Moving the wildlife out of the way as a first resort, or as a lazy remedy, has to be called out as straight-forwardly wrong.

We have to extend this principle to rebuilding a common home – a land – fit for all its human and non-human inhabitants to thrive in. I am not a land reformer by instinct, but I stand firmly on the side of those who wish to reform *ideas* about land. Who owns it matters less to me, but what we do with it matters to all, and if minority proprietorial interests are out of alignment with this, the common good must prevail.

We have to exercise creativity in understanding our place in nature, and reject the facile linear models of progress and binary choices that have brought us to a national and planetary tipping point. We have to allow the natural leaders of change, and demand of the *de jure* leaders of stasis, that they treat nature as a full partner in building the post-Covid future. Rebellion against extinction and loss may be an inevitable response when those who govern and who shape public discourse cannot be trusted with the future of the planet. But it need not be a permanent condition. Young people would not need to strike and take to the streets if they were given the right to participate fully in the political process. Conservation organisations should not shy away from championing the right of those who have the biggest stake in the future to have their say through the ballot box. After all, more common sense has been spoken by teenagers in the last two years than we have heard from the political elite in decades. Where's the harm?

Postscript

While the human world was shutting down and locking its doors, the non-human world continued nonchalantly to turn. One globe spun and tilted, making the days and the seasons happen and calling the birds from across the deserts; the other ground to half-speed, stretching the days and nights, casting the planes from the skies and emptying the streets. I finished this book in the early days of lockdown, and spent the following weeks inhabiting two and a half acres – or 0.000000002% – of the Earth's surface. It became a world within a world, and I found within it an infinity of other worlds. It was as if social disconnection had made all the other connections plainer, more readable.

At the forgotten beginning of 2020, in Davos-Klosters, Switzerland, the World Economic Forum held its 50th annual meeting. It was exactly three weeks after authorities in China had informed the World Health Organisation of a cluster of viral pneumonia cases of unknown cause in Wuhan. As the Forum opened on 21 January, there were 278 confirmed cases, all but four of them in China.

The 3,000 delegates gathered to review issues of global concern, which, for most of those fifty years have coalesced around the gravitational pull of global capital: wealth management, capital markets, and conventional threats such as international conflict. More recently, the Forum's annual headline theme has included words like rethink, redesign, new reality, transformation, new models, shared future and, appearing for the first time in 2020, 'sustainable'. The 2020 theme in full was *Stakeholders for a Cohesive and Sustainable World* and included several hours' worth of presentations and debate on the topic How to Save the Planet.

Ahead of the meeting, the WEF published a briefing titled Biodiversity Loss Puts Our Food Supplies and Medical Care at Risk – It Must Be Stopped. It was written not by an environmentalist or an academic ecologist, but by Peter Giger, Zurich Insurance Group's Chief Risk Officer. Environmental concerns dominated the list of most likely long-term risks presented in the forum's annual Global Risks Report, which noted that the current rate of biodiversity loss has critical implications for humanity, including the collapse of food and health systems.

Within weeks, that last scenario was suddenly real. The increasingly frequent emergence of new diseases was known to be linked to the degradation of ecological systems. Like some rare astrological alignment, a conjunction of the three great planetary concerns – economic, human and ecological well-being – had shown themselves to be a single, interconnected matter. The world's governments will be judged, therefore, on the interconnectedness or otherwise of the response. With no-one holding their breath to await such leadership, local initiatives by people feeling differently empowered have been emerging from the dark shadows of isolation. Flower-rich verges are left uncut, to enliven thousands of British towns and villages. Consortia of farmers[23] have used lockdown to launch initiatives aimed at "making things wilder – not to create space for nature but to find out how we live inside the ecosystem." Meanwhile in the July the World Economic Forum published a 111-page report calling for a critical shift towards nature-positive models in the three most damaging economic systems: food, land and ocean use; infrastructure and the built environment; mining and energy. Globally, a $2.7 trillion investment each year to 2030 would create 400 million jobs and $10 trillion a year in long-term business value, it said.[24] Is it conceivable, in these strange times, that the combined forces of local enterprise and global capital will give up waiting for any political impetus to invest in a green recovery and just do it anyway?

Notes, select bibliography and updates

Themes

1. Between 1566 and 1863 it was technically compulsory to kill species considered 'vermin' and for Parishes to pay bounties. Thereafter it was a matter for estates to decide on their own policy, and eventually more and more species were given legal protection. For the wildcat, this came as late as 1981, with the Wildlife and Countryside Act.
2. Darlene Johnston, *Connecting People to Place: Great Lakes Aboriginal History in a Cultural Context.* Ipperwash Inquiry Research Paper 2006
3. Dominic Dyer, CEO of the Badger Trust quoted in *The Independent* 18 December 2018
4. Dave Goulson, *Insect Declines and Why they Matter.* Report to the Wildlife Trusts 2020
5. Aldo Leopold, *A Sand County Almanac*, Oxford University Press 1949
6. Amphibian and Reptile Conservation, Bat Conservation Trust, Buglife, Bumblebee Conservation Trust, Butterfly Conservation, Plantlife and the RSPB, as well as the government conservation agency for England, Natural England. There are a further 90 organisations playing important roles in various projects within the programme, including, for the willow tit, the Yorkshire Wildlife Trust. In Wales and Scotland, similar partnerships have been working with their government agencies to develop equivalent programmes based on lessons learned during the initial English phase.
7. Efforts to save the species will continue, however. On 10 February 2020 a £5.5 million plan to breed them in captivity for release into a large designated area of the Cairngorms National Park was announced. The six-year effort to breed up to 60 animals will start in 2022, led by the Royal Zoological Society of Scotland.

8. Sainsbury, K. A., Shore, R. F., Schofield, H., Croose, E., Campbell, R. D. and McDonald, R. A. (2019), Recent history, current status, conservation and management of native mammalian carnivore species in Great Britain. *Mam Rev*, 49: 171–188. doi:10.1111/mam.12150

9. First published (posthumously) in 1891 and titled, of course, *"Hope" is the thing with feathers*. Dickinson was born in Amherst, Massachusetts in 1830 and died there in 1886.

Part 1 Portraits from Life

White-tailed eagle

1. Laurence Rose, *The Long Spring*. London: Bloomsbury 2018

2. This is guesswork. Pictish was almost certainly a Brittonic language, whose surviving forms all have similar-sounding words for the eagle: eryr (Welsh), er (Cornish), erer (Breton).

3. Old Norse *gjá* and *tangi* respectively.

4. Sheridan, J.A. (2010) Dating Scotland's Neolithic non-megalithic round mounds: new dates, problems and potential. In: Round mounds and monumentality in the British Neolithic and beyond. *Neolithic Studies Group Seminar Papers* (10). Oxbow Books, Oxford, pp. 28–52. ISBN 9781842174043

5. There may have been some special relationship for over 100,000 years: a recent re-examination of material excavated in 1901 from a 130,000-year old Neanderthal settlement in Croatia shows that the talons from four white-tailed eagles were collected to make some of the oldest known jewellery in Europe. See Radovčić D., Sršen A.O., Radovčić J., Frayer D.W. (2015) Evidence for Neanderthal Jewellery: Modified White-Tailed Eagle Claws at Krapina. PLoS ONE 10(3): e0119802. doi:10.1371/journal.pone.0119802

6. Yalden, D.W. (2007) The older history of the White-tailed Eagle in Britain. *Brit. Birds* 100: 471–480

7. There is strong circumstantial evidence for both, but the true location of the place known at the time as Brunanburh may never be known. However, in October 2019 Wirral Archaeology announced that they had compelling archaeological evidence from recent excavations that the site is, indeed, near Bromborough. However, the remains have yet to be formally analysed and published.

8. Anon. *Battle of Brunanburh* poem in the Anglo Saxon Chronicle. *Cambridge, Corpus Christi College, MS 173: The Parker Chronicle.*

9. To borrow from the Annals of Ulster's characterisation of the Battle of Brunanburh, as seen from Olaf's side.

10. For a comprehensive history of these Acts, their implementation, and persecution of so-called vermin generally, see Roger Lovegrove, *Silent Fields*. Oxford University Press 2007

11. Then equivalent to just under a halfpenny sterling.

12. George Low, *Fauna Orcadensis, or The Natural History of the Quadrupeds, Birds, Reptiles, and Fishes of Orkney and Shetland*. Edinburgh 1813

13. Probably hen harriers.

14. James Wallace, *Ane Account off the Ancient and Present State of Orkney*. Published posthumously and amended by his son in 1693. The quoted text is from the original handwritten manuscript, 1684

15. Gordon, J. (ed.) (1845) *New Statistical Account of Scotland*. General Assembly of the Church of Scotland.

16. Traditionally this last bird was spoken of as a female, but the only known photo of this (and of any native British) white-tailed eagle has been reidentified as almost certainly male.

17. There is a plausible eye-witness account of an active nest in northern Shetland in 1921 – see Love (2013), while the letter from J.G. Millais (page 34) also casts doubt.

18. John A. Love, *A Saga of Sea Eagles*. Whittles Publishing, 2013. This gives a comprehensive survey of past records, especially in Scotland, a wealth of information on incidents of persecution, and a first-hand account of the reintroduction schemes.

19. Roger Lovegrove *op. cit.*

20. Pennington et. al. (2004) reproduce an eye-witness account naming the perpetrator only as a clergyman called Sorby who came from Derby. I have searched the census records and The Rev. J. A. Sorby, born 1861 in Darley Dale, Derbyshire is the only likely candidate. *See* Pennington, M., Osborn, K., Harvey, P., Riddington, R., Okill, D., Ellis, P. and Heubeck, M. *The Birds of Shetland*. Helm, London 2004.

21. The Wild Birds Protection Act of 1880, amended in 1896 to allow County Councils to make Orders giving additional protections to specific birds and/or their eggs. The archaic spelling Zetland was in official use until 1974.

22. 1865–1931, son of Sir John Everett Millais, the founder of the Pre-Raphaelite Brotherhood of artists.

23. Stresemann, E. 1943 Überblick über die Vögel Kretas und den Vogelzug in der Ägäis. Unter Zugrundelegung der Tage bücher und Sammlungen Dr. Horst Siewerts. *J. Ornithol.* 91: 448–514.

24. On 10 March 2019 the ornithological world was shocked when the Observatory building was destroyed by fire with the loss of Waterston's handwritten diaries and personal library (but no human casualties). Plans for a new building were submitted for planning approval a year later.

25. Now owned and managed by the NCC's successor in Scotland, Scottish Natural Heritage.

26. Evans, R.J., O'Toole, L. and Whitfield, P. (2012) The history of eagles in Britain and Ireland: an ecological review of placename and documentary evidence from the last 1500 years. *Bird Study* 59:3, 335–349.

Corncrake

1. *Orkneyinga Saga and Magnus Saga with Appendices.* Editor Gudbrand Vigfusson. London: HMSO, 1887

2. Based on *Orkneyinga Saga: The History of the Earls of Orkney.* Translated by Hermann Pálsson and Paul Edwards. Penguin, London, 1978. The story of Paul/Pál and the otter hunt is chapter 74 in this translation, and chapter 78 in the Old Norse version cited above.

3. Plural of *cnoc* (outcrop).

4. Between 1995 and 2016, Britain's breeding starling population crashed by 51 per cent, with much heavier losses in England and lower declines in Scotland.

5. Machair: low-lying grassland that covers shell sand, a habitat almost unique to the Inner and Outer Hebrides and the north west shores of mainland Scotland and of Ireland.

6. *Thus passit furth quhill June, that jolie tyde, / And seidis that wer sawin off beforne / Wer growin hie, that hairis mycht thame hyde, / And als the quailze craikand in the corne. / I movit furth betuix midday and morne / Unto the hedge under the hawthorne grene, / Quhair I befoir the said birdis had sene.* Robert Henryson (c. 1430–1505) Translation by Laurence Rose.

7. Body very compressed; in the evening and at night – loud call, a double crex.

8. *The Landrail* (1832) by John Clare (1793–1864)

9. *The Shepherd's Calendar – May* (1820)

10. Richard Jeffries, *Nightingale Road* in *Nature Near London* London: Chatto & Windus 1883

11. D.H. Lawrence, *Sons and Lovers.* London: Gerald Duckworth and Co., 1913

12. D.H. Lawrence, *The White Peacock.* London: Heinemann, 1911

13. D.H. Lawrence, *The Rainbow.* London: Methuen and Co., 1915

14. D.H. Lawrence, final stanza from *End of Another Home Holiday* (1909). In his short story *The Overtone* (1933) there is yet another description of a moonlight and corncrake-infused nightfall as the setting for an unsettled mind, that of the lovelorn Will Renshaw.

15. Andrew Marvell (1621–1678). From the 776-line *Upon Appleton House*, describing the estate of Lord Thomas Fairfax.

16. Geolocator tagging of birds breeding on the island of Coll has shown that corncrakes undertake a double migration, flying to western Africa first and then on to the western part of the Congo basin. It is suspected that they winter in open areas within the forest such as those cleared by forest elephants. This work will enable factors such as changing rainfall or overgrazing in the Congo to be analysed, to see whether there is any correlation with changes in breeding populations on Coll.

17. Scything styles varied: as William Marshall, the agricultural writer noted in 1798, "The Yorkshireman drives a width of nine or ten feet before him, the Gloucestershireman of six or seven feet only."

18. See www.hayinart.com

19. *Barnsley Chronicle*, Saturday 31 July 1909

20. *Sheffield Daily Telegraph*, Thursday 13 June 1929

21. G.A. Tyler , R.E. Green & C. Casey (1998) Survival and behaviour of Corncrake *Crex crex* chicks during the mowing of agricultural grassland, *Bird Study*, 45:1, 35–50, DOI: 10.1080/00063659809461076

22. Mike Shrubb, *Birds, Scythes and Combines: a history of birds and agricultural change*. Cambridge: Cambridge University Press, 2003.

23. Alexander, H.G. (1914) A report on the Land-Rail inquiry. *Brit. Birds* 8: 82–92

24. The inquiry contradicts some of the published accounts in the county avifaunas: in Yorkshire, for example, it is described as "still fairly plentiful in the Wolds" *contra* Mather.

25. Norris, C.A. (1947). Report on the Distribution and Status of the Corn Crake. *Brit. Birds* 40:226–244

26. In July 2019 it was announced that two pairs of corncrakes were breeding on Rathlin Island, after 17 years of targeted habitat management by local farmers in association with the RSPB. There has been a small breeding population in Yorkshire's Lower Derwent Valley in most years since at least 2010, the only naturally-occurring English population left. A reintroduction programme is underway in locations in Cambridgeshire and Norfolk.

27. The most recent revision of birds' conservation status puts the number of European species at risk of extinction as 39, a list that does not include the corncrake, following a reassessment of its status outside Europe.

28. Borja Heredia, Laurence Rose and Mary Painter (eds.), *Globally Threatened Birds in Europe: Action Plans*. Strasbourg: Council of Europe, 1996

Fox

1. This being rural Yorkshire, foxes here are largely nocturnal and generally nervous of humans. I have seen them in our nearest large town, Huddersfield, by street-light, and any visit to London can yield wonderful, prolonged views by night or day. In my former home town of Swanley, Kent I used to watch them courting and fighting in the street from an upstairs window. Even such everyday behaviour is something I have yet to witness in this rural setting.

2. Department of Environment, Food and Rural Affairs.

3. I do not feed and film the animals every night, but on average about one night in three, at irregular intervals; this avoids them becoming

dependent, and hopefully avoids too high a level of interaction between them and other local foxes that might not visit as frequently under natural conditions.

4. Over the winter of 2019 Spot-smudge and Blankles were again paired. Sadly, Spot-smudge appeared in the camera footage of 23 November 2019 displaying a fresh, serious injury to the right side of his face. By the following night his right eye had closed. Over the succeeding seven weeks he continued to appear before the camera, apparently coping with one eye. Then, on 15 January he appeared with a severe limp due to an injured left hind leg. Five days later the limp had improved, but it was the last time I saw him. His sister Harlequin became an infrequent visitor, but appeared several times during February and early March 2020, obviously pregnant again.

5. Anon c.1380 *Sir Gawayn and þe Grene Knygt*. Based on the Middle English text edited by J.R.R Tolkien and E.V. Gordon (Oxford, Clarendon Press 1930 edition), translated by Laurence Rose.

6. A cross between a beagle and an Old English hound.

7. Since the hunting ban, the seasons have been maintained and the function of the activities changed to comply with the law, with frequent incidences of non-compliance reported. Dates are variable and not determined by legislation, unlike, for example, game shooting. The full season is when the fox (pre-ban) or trail (post-ban) hunt as it is generally understood, takes place and typically runs between 1 November and 31 March or into April; the Autumn season, formerly and still occasionally known as the cubbing season, runs from harvest, often late July, until the end of September, when young foxes are dispersed and novice hounds trained. The closed season is generally regarded as the start of the hunting year, and is characterised by puppy sales, country shows and leaving parties for hunt staff moving to new appointments.

8. Roger Lovegrove *op. cit.*

9. Pringle, H., Wilson, M., Calladine, J., Siriwardena, G. (2019) Associations between gamebird releases and generalist predators. *J. Appl. Ecol.* 56: 2102–2113

10. ECHR Decision on Friend and Others v. United Kingdom 24 November 2009

11. Howe, J. (1981) Fox Hunting as Ritual. *American Ethnologist* 8: 278–300

Badger

1. The advantage over foxes is much less pronounced, as they have rather good night vision and superb hearing.

2. For reasons that will become clear, this description of the area in question is partially disguised.

3. *Bovine TB: The Scientific Evidence.* Final Report of the Independent Scientific Group on Cattle TB, 2007

4. In for the cull. *Nature* 450, 1–2 (2007) doi:10.1038/450001b

5. Downs, S.H., Prosser, A., Ashton, A. *et al.* Assessing effects from four years of industry-led badger culling in England on the incidence of bovine tuberculosis in cattle, 2013–2017. *Sci Rep* 9, 14666 (2019) doi:10.1038/s41598–019–49957–6

6. Ham, C., Donnelly, C.A., Astley, K.L., Jackson, S.Y.B., Woodroffe, R. (2019) Effect of culling on individual badger *Meles meles* behaviour: Potential implications for bovine tuberculosis transmission. *J. Appl. Ecol.* 56: 2390–2399

7. The devolved administration in Wales has ruled out widespread badger culling in favour of a mixed vaccination, testing and selective cull policy. Scotland, where there is no badger culling, has more stringent cattle movement rules and been officially bTB-free (meaning that bTB is detected in less than 0.1% of animals for at least six years) since 2009.

8. Godfray, C. (2018). *A strategy for achieving Bovine Tuberculosis Free Status for England: 2018 review.* Report to Rt. Hon Michael Gove MP, Secretary of State, DEFRA.

9. A neurodegenerative disease of cattle. British cattle were infected in large numbers between 1986 and 2006 through the then-widespread practice of feeding cows a high-protein feed supplement made from the remains of other animals. Over four million cows were slaughtered in an effort to contain the outbreak, and 177 people died after contracting variant Creutzfeldt-Jakob disease through eating infected beef.

10. The proportion of herds with bovine TB in the Gloucestershire pilot zone increased from 6.9% at the start of culling to 9% over the five-year period. The rate of occurrence of new confirmed bovine TB cases – known as the incidence rate – was 13.2% in 2018, compared with 12.7% when the cull began in 2013. In Somerset, the incidence rate declined, but the disease had become more widespread across herds. The official data show that the proportion of herds with bovine TB increased from 6.1% when culling started to 6.7% at the end of 2018.

11. Harris, S., (1993) The Status of the badger (*Meles meles*) in Britain with particular reference to East Anglia. *Trans. Suffolk Nat. Soc.* 29: 104–112

12. Neal, E., (1972) The National Badger Survey. *Mammal Rev.* 2: 55–64

13. Judge J., Wilson G.J., Macarthur R., McDonald R.A., Delahay R.J. (2017) Abundance of badgers (*Meles meles*) in England and Wales. Scientific Reports 7: 276.

14. Sainsbury, K. A., Shore, R. F., Schofield, H., Croose, E., Campbell, R. D. and McDonald, R. A. (2019), Recent history, current status, conservation and management of native mammalian carnivore species in Great Britain. *Mam Rev*, 49: 171–188. doi:10.1111/mam.12150

15. Comprising the two largest towns of Huddersfield and Dewsbury, several small mill towns such as Batley and Cleckheaton and numerous villages.

A substantial proportion is rural, including some sparsely-populated uplands.

16. Not the site's real name, and some other details have been disguised.

17. Ritchie, M. et al. (2018) *Bovine TB: time for a rethink* http://www.rethinkbtb.org/rethink_documents/BTB_rethink_2nd_edition.pdf

Update August 2020: the new strategy purports to focus on the 94% of herds infected by other cattle, rather than the 6% infected by badgers. However the government has not kept its promise to pilot badger vaccination in areas in which culling licences have expired. Instead, it licensed another five years of culling on all the land that would have been eligible for a pilot. They also published proposals to facilitate culling around vaccinated land, especially in Derbyshire. I and thousands of others have contributed to legal challenges.

Willow tit

1. First published in *Zi-Zi Taah Taah Taah: the song of the willow tit.* (Poems by Steve Ely). Wild West Press 2018. Dr Steve Ely is Senior Lecturer in Creative Writing at the University of Huddersfield and Director of the Ted Hughes Network. *Oswald's Book of Hours*, his first published book of poetry and *Englaland*, his second, were published by Smokestack in 2013 and 2015. He recently completed *Made in Mexborough: Ted Hughes's South Yorkshire*, a biographical work about the late Laureate's neglected Mexborough period.

2. The main character in *A Kestrel for a Knave*, the 1968 novel by Hoyland Common born author Barry Hines (1939–2016), adapted a year later as the film *Kes* by Hines and Ken Loach.

3. Young Ornithologists' Club, the name of the RSPB's junior branch between 1965 and 2000, now the Wildlife Explorers.

4. Local Wildlife Sites are formally recognised for their importance locally and may influence local planning decisions, while having no national-level protection, unlike SSSIs, which are nationally designated and subject to certain protective measures and management requirements. See also p. 261 for the full impact of all three phases of the project.

5. Opening 4 lines of 2nd stanza.

6. Rothschild, W. (1907) The British Willow Tit (*Parus atricapillus kleinschmidti* Hellm.) *Brit. Birds* 1: 44–47

7. For me, and as Steve noted at South Kirkby, the birds' shape is helpful, too. The marsh tit has a more obvious neck, which in the willow tit is much more muscular, so that the line of the head and the body is smooth, and bird more plum-shaped. This extra musculature is an adaptation allowing the willow tit to excavate its own nest-hole.

8. Lewis, A.J.G., Amar, A., Piec, D. & Thewlis, R.M., 2007, Factors influencing Willow Tit *Poecile montanus* site occupancy: A comparison of abandoned and occupied woods. *Ibis* 149: 205–213

9. The initial phase of Back from the Brink runs from April 2017 to the end of 2020, funded by National Lottery Heritage Fund, People's Postcode Lottery, the Esmée Fairbairn Foundation, The EU Life fund, The Garfield Weston Foundation, the Patsy Wood Trust. The willow tit project also benefited from additional funding from Veolia Environmental Trist.

Update: the 2020 willow tit survey was cancelled, along with most other field work across the country, due to the Covid-19 outbreak. Just prior to the lockdown in late March, I visited the Broggs and the Tunnel End, where a pair was present and apparently occupying the same territory.

Field cricket

1. Maturity
2. Letter XLVI (1779, undated) to the Hon. Daines Barrington in White, Gilbert (1789), *The Natural History and Antiquities of Selborne*.
3. Gilbert White, *op. cit.*
4. Virgil *Ecl*.2.12–13
5. Sutton, P.G., Beckmann, B.C. & Nelson, B. (2017) The current status of Orthopteroid insects in Britain and Ireland. *Atropos* 59: 6–33
6. see p. 11
7. Huntley, B., Green, R.E., Collingham, Y.C., and S.G. Willis, *A Climatic Atlas of European Breeding Birds.* Durham University, The RSPB and Lynx Editions, Barcelona, 2007
8. Green, E.J. (2017) Population responses to climate change of two European warbler species. PhD Thesis, University of Cambridge.
9. Gilbert White, part of the same letter.
10. Charles Darwin, *On the Origin of Species.* London: John Murray 1859
11. *Oryctes nasicornis*
12. Contributors: *The stark bare wood of an old stump breaks through the greenery in act of defiance* [Jane Sears]; *dead but still alive* and *one of the invertebrate Big Five* [Chloë Bradford]. *Bleached bones* and *charismatic microfauna* [Elinor Newman].
13. Mark Twain, *The Adventures of Tom Sawyer*, 1876.

Narrow-headed ant

1. Bert Hölldobler and Edward O. Wilson, *The Ants.* Harvard University Press 1990
2. In the UK there are about 24,500 insect species alone –1,800 'true' bugs, 4,000 beetles, 7,000 flies and 7,000 species of bees, wasps and ants. The invertebrate conservation charity Buglife uses 40,000 as an educated rough estimate for invertebrates as a whole, whilst acknowledging that no-one really knows.

3. Estimates vary enormously, and no-one really knows, but based on Dave Goulson's view that there are perhaps 5 million insects in the world, this would seem a reasonable estimate for the total number of invertebrates.

4. Gilbert White, Letter XXXV to Daines Barrington, May 20, 1777 *op. cit.* As this was in a letter concerning earthworms, he presumably used the word 'reptile' in the literal sense of 'creeping/crawling thing' before it became exclusively used to denominate the vertebrate class Reptilia.

5. The synthetic organochloride insecticide Dichlorodiphenyltrichloroethane.

6. I have amalgamated the conversations that follow from the two separate visits, on 8 October 2018 and 5 September 2019, the second of which was with Stephen alone.

7. Sibelco later explained that the drilling was to establish the depth of clay and its quality, and that "whilst there will always be an option to quarry, this is not envisaged in the next 10 to 15 years."

8. *Callipterinella tuberculata* and *Symydobius oblongus* respectively.

9. Sánchez-Bayo, F. and Wyckhuys, K.A.G. (2019). Worldwide decline of the entomofauna: a review of its drivers. *Biological Conservation* 232: 8–27

Otter

1. Here I use the convention in historical linguistics of prefixing a reconstructed word that is not recorded in texts with an asterisk, as in *wed-*.

2. Dylan Thomas, *Poem in October* (1944)

3. See page 44.

4. Chanin, P. & Jefferies, D.J. (1978) The decline of the otter *Lutra lutra* L. in Britain: an analysis of hunting records and discussion of causes. *Biol. J. Linn. Soc.* 10: 305–328

5. Mason C.F., Ford T.C., Last, N.I. (1986) Organochlorine residues in British otters. *Bulletin of Environmental Contamination and Toxicology* 36: 656– 661

6. Although dieldrin is most commonly cited as the cause of otter decline, polychlorinated biphenyls (PCBs) may also have contributed by impairing reproduction in individuals not poisoned by dieldrin. See Sainsbury *et. al.* (2019) *op. cit.*

7. Watt, J. (1993) Ontogeny of hunting behaviour in otters (*Lutra lutra* L.) in a marine environment. *Symposia of the Zoologicial Society of London* 65: 87–104

8. Outhwaite, C.L., Gregory, R.D., Chandler, R.E. et al. (2020) Complex long-term biodiversity change among invertebrates, bryophytes and lichens. *Nat. Ecol. Evol.* https://doi.org/10.1038/s41559-020-1111-z

9. Kean E.F., Lyons G., & Chadwick E.A. (2013) Persistent organic pollutants and indicators of otter health. A CHEM Trust report.

10. Nitrate Vulnerable Zones are areas designated as posing a risk to water courses from agricultural nitrate pollution. Farms in these areas are subject to compulsory measures including governing the use of inorganic nitrate fertiliser and the storage of organic fertilisers.

11. See, for example, successive State of Nature Reports, which are produced every three years as a synthesis of data compiled by over 50 organisations. The most recent was published in 2019 and assessed the status and trends in 8,418 species in the UK, finding that 15% are at risk of extinction.

Nightingale

1. *Macbeth* Act III scene II: Light thickens; and the crow makes wing to the rooky wood: good things of day begin to droop and drowse.

2. Mark Cocker, *Our Place: can we save Britain's wildlife before it is too late*? Jonathan Cape, 2018.

3. Hewson, CM, Miller, M, Johnston, A, et al. (2018) Estimating national population sizes: Methodological challenges and applications illustrated in the common nightingale, a declining songbird in the UK. *J Appl Ecol.* 55: 2008– 2018. https://doi.org/10.1111/1365–2664.13120

4. Moore, J.M., Székely, T., Büki, J. &Timothy J. DeVoogd, T.J. (2011) Motor pathway convergence predicts syllable repertoire size in oscine birds. *Proceedings of the National Academy of Sciences* DOI: 10.1073/pnas.1102077108. (Bizarrely, HVC stands for nothing at all, and is the full name of the brain segment in question. Once known as the Hyperstriatum Ventrale pars Caudatus, later re-named High Vocal Centre, and with both names since deemed incorrect, the acronym is all that remains.)

5. Stesichorus (c. 630 – 555 BCE) was the first great lyric poet of the West. His style was thought comparable to the voice of the nightingale, according to the Palatine Anthology: "...at his birth, when he had just reached the light of day, a nightingale, travelling through the air from somewhere or other, perched unnoticed on his lips and struck up her clear song." Pliny the Elder, *Natural History* Book X, XLIII

6. Amrhein, V., Korner, P. & Naguib, M. (2002) Nocturnal and diurnal singing activity in the nightingale: correlations with mating status and breeding cycle. *Animal Behaviour* 64: 939–944

7. Huntley, B., Green, R.E., Collingham, Y.C., and S.G. Willis, *A Climatic Atlas of European Breeding Birds.* Durham University, The RSPB and Lynx Editions, Barcelona, 2007

8. see Sansum, P., McKernan, P., Westaway, S. and Grose, M. (2009) *A revision of the Ancient Woodland Inventory for Ashford Borough, Kent* High Weald AONB Unit Project carried out by the Weald and Downs Ancient Woodland Survey for East Sussex and Kent November 2006 to March 2009

9. Department of Environment, Food and Rural Affairs

10. HLS (in England), Glastir (in Wales), the Agri-Environment Climate Scheme (in Scotland) and the Environmental Farming Scheme (NI) fund 10-year (or longer) agreements for the more ambitious agri-environment measures. In 2021 payments on offer include measures for species rich grasslands, wet grassland and water meadows; heathland and moorland; coastal sand dunes, vegetated shingle, saltmarsh, inter-tidal and saline habitats; fens, reedbeds, ponds and ditches; wood pastures and parklands, orchards, hedges and scrub; woodland and may also give grants to protect vulnerable or threatened species.

11. Isabella Tree, *Wilding*, Picador 2018

12. Holt, C.A., Hewson, C.M. and Fuller, R.J. (2012) The Nightingale in Britain: status, ecology and conservation needs. *Brit. Birds* 105: 172–187

13. Netherlands Institute of Ecology. *Winter Moth Proves Able To Adjust To Climate Change.* ScienceDaily, 21 June 2007.

14. If only it were that simple: In 2019 a group of scientists collated a database of all known birds, bryophytes, fungi, invertebrates, lichens and mammals that use oak (*Quercus petraea* and *Q. robur*) in the UK, a total of 2300 species, including 326 that are completely dependent on oak. See Mitchell, R.J., Bellamy, P.E., Ellis, C.J., Hewison, R.L., Hodgetts, N.G., Iason, G.R., Littlewood, N.A., Newey, S., Stockan, J.A. and Taylor, A.F.S. (2019) Collapsing foundations: The ecology of the British oak, implications of its decline and mitigation options. *Biol. Cons.* 233: 316–327

15. Julian Hoffman, *Irreplaceable: the fight to save our wild places.* London: Hamish Hamilton 2019

16. SSSIs were established, alongside National Parks and Areas of Outstanding Natural Beauty, in 1949 by the National Parks and Access to the Countryside Act. The legal framework has since been devolved within the UK (with diverging criteria for designation and standards of enforcement) and amended by successive legislation. Often a site carries an additional designation, such as a Special Area of Conservation under EU law, but it is the SSSI system that provides the formal legislative and enforcement framework. 'Protection' amounts to ensuring an SSSI's features are considered alongside other considerations, giving substantial leeway for local planning authorities to overturn the protection given, subject, if challenged, to the final say of the Secretary of State.

Part 2 Landscapes of Change

Vanishing Points

1. *To a Skylark* (1820), 18th stanza.
2. Scholes, R.J. and Biggs, R. (2005) A biodiversity intactness index. *Nature* 434: 45–49.
3. The modelled average abundance of originally-present species, relative to their abundance in an intact ecosystem.
4. The English Indices of Deprivation 2015. Department for Communities and Local Government
5. Goulson, D., Croombs, A. and Thompson, J. (2018). Rapid rise in toxic load for bees revealed by analysis of pesticide use in Great Britain. *PEERJ* 6:e5255
6. This may be a dramatic under-estimate, since this figure was established by the late Sir Richard Body, agricultural author and MP for South Lincolnshire between 1966 and 2001. He undertook his own stock-take of farming during the overproduction scandals of the late 20th century, calculating that we had lost 130,000 small farmers in the two decades to 1982.
7. Gullone E. (2000), The Biophilia hypothesis and life in the 21st century: increasing mental health or increasing pathology? *Journal of Happiness Studies*. 1: 293–321.
8. Perkins, H.E. (2010), Measuring love and care for nature. *Journal of Environmental Psychology*. 2010; 30: 455–463.
9. *Scientific American* 1 March 2012
10. *The Guardian* 5 October 2018
11. Lumber R, Richardson M, Sheffield D (2017) Beyond knowing nature: Contact, emotion, compassion, meaning, and beauty are pathways to nature connection. *PLoS ONE* 12(5): e0177186
12. Life stories: books about a planet in peril *The Guardian* 4 October 2019
13. Organised by People, Landscape and Cultural Environment or PLACE. These paragraphs are a slightly edited version of the concluding part of a paper I contributed to the conference proceedings, and I am grateful for PLACE's permission to use them here. See also Rose, L. (2020) Bird Conservation: from citizen science to nature citizenship *in:* Atherden, M. and Wallace, V. (eds.) The Changing *Nature* of Conservation. PLACE in press.
14. Mark Cocker *op. cit.*
15. I was speaking nearly a year before the government announced its intention to phase out the badger cull over five years, dependent on a cattle vaccine being developed. In my view, had the investment in the cull been directed at finding a cattle vaccine from the outset, this would have been achieved by now.
16. See p. 7

17. Discourse on the Method of Rightly Conducting One's Reason and of Seeking Truth in the Sciences (*Discours de la Méthode Pour bien conduire sa raison, et chercher la vérité dans les sciences*)
18. Fritjof Capra (b. 1939) is an Austrian-born American physicist, systems theorist and deep ecologist. He is a founding director of the Center for Ecoliteracy in Berkeley, California and is a former teacher at Schumacher College.
19. David Orr, *Earth in Mind*. Washington: Island Press 1994

From Stones to Humankind

1. Between 2008 and at least November 2011 there were no recorded attacks in Mumbai. Then seven or eight, four of them fatal, in the following 23 months to October 2013, most of them in Aarey Colony, a forested area outside SGNP, which had seen a wave of urban development, as well as new illegal encroachments. This spike in the casualty rate may be attributable to one or two animals whose behaviour changed due to the sudden increase of uncontrolled garbage, or to illness, old age, or loss of territory to other leopards. There were no further fatalities until one in 2017. At the time of my visit in October 2018, the only incident that year had involved a Rottwelier dog that had been tied up outside a dwelling at night.
2. The closest western equivalent would be C-Db-E-F-Gb-Ab-B-C
3. The 'wandering' sense – to western ears – is likely due to the even stranger tone row, roughly equivalent to B-Db-E-F#-A-B-Db-C. To more attuned ears, it could be better described as 'contemplative'.
4. What follows is Manisha's interpretation, but her version was necessarily a rushed précis of what I assume was a more detailed, wide-ranging conversation with few pauses to allow full translation.
5. Hardabhai spoke rapidly and almost continuously, and here Manisha was trying to interpret in real time. Her exact words were: "we don't have negativity, we are laughing... not laughing, but we don't have that negativity towards lion." *Embrace* is my attempt to find a word – barely adequate I am sure – for what would appear to be a very complex balance of emotions.

Update July 2020: this year at least 87 lions died of disease, 32 of them known to have succumbed to a return of canine distemper in combination with babesiosis; tests are due on the others, who are also suspected victims.

Perspective and *Postscript*

1. Richard Mabey, *The Common Ground – a place for nature in Britain's future?* Hutchinson and Co., 1980.
2. The NCC was established (as the Nature Conservancy) by the National Parks and Access to the Countryside Act 1949, and eventually replaced in 1990 by three country-level agencies (Northern Ireland was not included) along with a smaller non-statutory body, the Joint Nature Conservation Committee, to oversee residual UK-level responsibilities. Holliday resigned over the government's failure to consult NCC over the impending change.
3. In its original guise as the European Economic Community.
4. Spaak, Paul-Henri. (1956) *Intergovernmental Committee on European Integration. The Brussels Report on the General Common Market.*
5. Heinrich Böll Foundation (2019) *Agriculture Atlas 2019.*
6. Killer Slime, Dead Birds, an Expunged Map: The Dirty Secrets of European Farm Subsidies, *New York Times,* 25 December 2019
7. https://www.arc2020.eu/agriculture-atlas-tied-to-the-land/
8. *New York Times, op. cit.*
9. EU Court of Auditors Press Release 12 December 2017. *Greening the CAP: income support more complex and not yet environmentally effective, say EU Auditors.*
10. *Independent* 19 December 2012
11. Michael McCarthy, *The Moth Snowstorm: nature and joy.* London: Hachette 2015
12. See *Corncrake* (chapter 2)
13. The rival claimants to have been the progenitor of the expression (or the adverbial alternative *Think globally, Act locally*) include David Brower, founder of Friends of the Earth, French-American microbiologist and environmentalist René Dubos, and Canadian futurist Frank Feather.
14. *Financial Times* 20 January 2020
15. The Wildlife Trusts (2020) *What's the Damage? Why HS2 will cost nature too much.*
16. Nature Improvement Areas were established to create ecological networks at a landscape scale and are run by partnerships of local authorities, landowners, and conservation organisations with funding from DEFRA and Natural England. Living Landscapes are similarly areas where the Wildlife Trusts network is working in partnership, for example working with landowners to restore peat bogs in the uplands.
17. Lawton, J. (2010) *Making Space for Nature.* Report to DEFRA.
18. i.e. when atmospheric CO_2 reached 400 parts per million [in 2016]. Amitav Ghosh, *The Great Derangement: climate change and the unthinkable,* The University of Chicago Press, 2016
19. see https://www.cbd.int/sp/targets/
20. *The Guardian* 28 October 2015
21. See page 206
22. See page 126

23. For example, the WildEast consortium of three Suffolk and Norfolk farmers aiming to persuade other landowners, councils etc. to join them in devoting 25% of their land to nature see www.wildeast.co.uk
24. World Economic Forum, 2020. *New Nature Economy Report II: The Future of Nature and Business.*

Acknowledgements

My research for these essays was hugely helped by a number of people who spent time with me in the field, particularly Debbie Bailey, Tim Birch and Georgie Hutton of the Derbyshire Wildlife Trust and Clive Turner, Sue Shaw and members of the Kirklees Badger Protection Group (badgers); Steve Ely (willow tit), to whom I am also grateful for permission to reproduce his poem *Poecile montana kleinschmidti*; Mike Coates, Jane Sears, Peter Sheppard Skærved and Mihailo Trandafilovksi (field cricket); Stephen Carroll and John Walters (narrow-headed ant); Sam Lee and Corin Stuart (nightingales).

A special thanks to Manisha Rajput and Krishna Tiwari for organising and facilitating my discussions with the Warli, Kokna and Maldhari people in Mumbai and Gujarat, and to the interviewees themselves, especially those named in the essay *From Stones to Humankind* (chapter 11). Also to Bhushan Pandya, Revtubha Raijana, Devvrat and Druv Bhatt, Stalin Dyanand, Nandakumar Pawar, Rajesh Sanap and Ranjeet Jadhav for their inspiring conversation. My research in India was an RSPB sabbatical project, and I am grateful to the RSPB for this support.

Many other people have helped in a variety of ways, especially Nadine Andrews, Vidya Athreya, Mike and Jan Bax,

Chris Bowden, Jon Bramley, Adrian Broadbent, Emma Burt, Kartik Chandramouli, Sujan Chatterjee, Mark Cocker, Andy Evans, Sara Evans, Joe Glentworth, James Harding-Morris, Stephen Hedley, Julian Hoffman, Ziad Ibbini, Peregrine and Dee Massey, Dinah and Peter North, Susannah O'Riordan, Sophie Pinder, Miles Richardson, Martin and MaryAnn Richmond-Coggan, Julian Rush, Dave Sexton, Adrian Thomas, Chris Tomson and Laura and Andrew Willan. My colleagues Andrew Bibby, Chiz Dakin, Christopher Goddard, Andrew McCloy and Colin Speakman at Gritstone Publishing cooperative, and Lucy Frontani and Penny Hayashi at Carnegie Book Production have given the project great encouragement and helpful advice. This is the second book on which I have collaborated with the artist Richard Allen, whose involvement has again made a big difference. My brother David Rose created the narrative separator images. Jane Rose has again been a tremendous support, especially in literature research, proof-reading, editing, logistics and general advice and encouragement.

Index

Wilson, Edward O. 9–12, 157
Wilson, Harold 247
Winchester 187
winter moth 204–5
Wisbech (Cambridgeshire) 213
wolf 30, 82, 90
woodlark 148, 156
Woodroffe, Prof. Rosie 100
World Economic Forum 273–4
World War I 62, 86, 126
World War II 35, 63, 67, 87, 179, 214
Worldwide Fund for Nature 264

X
XR *see* Extinction Rebellion

Y
Yalden, Derek 29, 39
Yamuna River 270
Yangtze river dolphin 263
yellowhammer 68, 70, 134
York 55, 124, 220, 264
Yorkshire 59, 61, 63, 103, 126, 192, 246
North 14
South 29, 107–8, 192
West 13, 65, 72, 107
Yorkshire Wildlife Trust 135
Carlton Marsh reserve 119–20

Z
Zoological Society of London 101, 140